A Journey Round My Skull

A JOURNEY ROUND MY SKULL

by
FRIGYES KARINTHY

——— ◆ ———

translated from the Hungarian by
Vernon Duckworth Barker

with a preface by
Mihály Sükösd

CORVINA

Originally published in Hungarian as
Utazás a koponyám körül, 1938

First published in Englis in February 1939 by
Faber and Faber Limited,
24 Russell Square, London
This second edition published
by Corvina Books, Budapest
(Vörösmarty tér 1. Hungary 1051)
by permission of Faber and Faber
Limited, London

Design by Judit Kállói
Series design by András Török
Cover illustration by András Felvidéki

ISBN 963 13 2525 3

Printed in Hungary, 1992

Szekszárd Printing House, Szekszárd

Karinthy and A Journey Round My Skull

In the following pages I shall attempt to introduce the work of the Hungarian writer Frigyes Karinthy to the English-speaking reader. The task I have set myself is by no means an easy one. Karinthy was undoubtedly one of the outstanding writers of the first half of the twentieth century, a fact which will have already been clear to just about any Hungarian, but which for English-speaking readers may require some explanation.

By way of introduction I might start by noting that in Budapest, the Hungarian capital, there is a street named after Karinthy – the street where I happen to live. I might also add that another building in the street where Karinthy lived in the 1930s is today marked by a plaque erected in his honour. The café where he spent many pleasant afternoons, and which provided him with a frequent setting for this book, is today the site of a modern drinking establishment.

In describing all this to my imaginary reader I fear that I am running up against powerful obstacles. I've frequently found that even the most erudite English readers have problems navigating through the complicated historical and geographical boundaries of East-Central Europe. It's accomplishment enough when Budapest, the capital of my country, is not confused with Bucharest, that of a neighbouring country. There is nothing for it therefore: this introduction must start with a mention of some basic biographical, literary, and historical facts, without which no thorough discussion of the writer's career can be complete.

Frigyes Karinthy was born in Budapest in 1887 and died at a country resort in 1938. He was 51 years old at the time. Apart from summer vacations and several stays abroad of varying duration, he spent his entire life in Budapest.

Once upon a time, over the course of many decades, there was an incredible empire, the Austro-Hungarian Monarchy. The images of this empire that have reached the wider world were primarily conveyed by writers whose work was in German, writers such as Kafka, Musil, and Joseph Roth. Their German mode of expression was more suited to translation and reception abroad than the "barbarian" language used by the best of their Hungarian contemporaries.

That the Monarchy disintegrated in the revolutions following the First World War is a well-known fact. An independent Hungary was established and the transitional months of uncertainty were followed in 1920 by the partly fascist, partly bourgeois democratic regime of Rear-Admiral and Regent Nicholas Horthy. This hybrid system remained operative right up until 1944.

Frigyes Karinthy was both a native and an inhabitant of this world – perhaps a rather narrow one when viewed through English eyes, but a field for immense experience, given the circumstances in Hungary. Karinthy was an urban, middle-class writer – designations which should possibly be explained a little more thoroughly. To be an urban writer in Hungary during the first half of this century meant – and to a certain extent still means – that the person in question came from a middle-class family, spent the better part of his life in the capital, and drew most of his experiences and observations from this citified environment. However, since in the early twentieth century Hungary was still essentially an agrarian country, where the peasantry played a much greater role than either the urban working class or the intelligentsia, an urban middle-class writer could never compete with writers portraying the life of the country-dwelling Hungarian peasant or bourgeois writers such as Móricz Zsigmond, the greatest Hungarian novelist of the first part of the century.

In short, Karinthy belonged to the middle class, and resided in the city. Moreover, he was of Jewish descent, although he came from a family which had converted to Christianity. Although his Jewish origins were not directly. disadvantageous to Karinthy, it must be said that they were not particularly helpful given the character of the Horthy regime, especially during the last years of his life, when anti-Semitism was growing in Hungary. His career and life-style were forced to conform to these harsh realities.

Karinthy enrolled at several universities, but never finished any of them. He never became a *poeta doctus*, remaining a free-lance writer and journalist until the end of his life. He delved into a great variety of subjects, primarily philosophy, medicine and – departing somewhat from the interests of his contemporaries – the applied sciences.

How did all of this contribute to the development of his career as a writer?

3

While the volume of Karinthy's work is prodigious, its quality is at times rather uneven. He wrote philosophical poems, short stories, novels, plays, studies, humorous sketches, and an enormous number of newspaper articles, all with varying results and varying success. Reading his work, one can sense that much of it was done to make money as quickly as possible, and that it was often rushed off at the last minute.

Karinthy left an enduring mark on two genres – the literary parody and the novel. In the 1920s he became nationally renowned for his outstanding parodies of contemporaries, the leading Hungarian writers of the time. It is unfortunate that this brilliant genre attracted – and continues to attract – only Hungarian readers. The world outside Hungary could not enjoy Karinthy's literary parodies, if only because of the formidable difficulties in translating Hungarian. Yet Karinthy's admirable gift for parodying language and style ranks his works – in the opinion of the present writer at least – alongside that of Stephen Leacock, the author of *Literary Lapses*.

In the final analysis, a writer's reputation is decided by that part of his work which remains of lasting value, those of his works posterity endeavours to preserve. Viewed from this perspective, Karinthy's lasting contribution has been his novels.

As we shall presently show, Karinthy was a student of the English and French Enlightenment in twentieth-century Hungary. As a novelist he learned the most from Swift. Two of Karinthy's better-known novels, *Travels to Faremido* and *Travels to Capillaria*, owe allegiance to the Swiftian tradition, so much so that they can be seen as the fictive fifth and sixth journeys of Captain Gulliver. Both employ the narrative technique of *Gulliver's Travels*, using Swift's method to the point of exaggeration – at times even to parody. The novels are not simply thematic – they are moral tracts made intelligible for the general reader disguised in novel form. *Travels to Faremido* was published in 1916 and in it Karinthy portrays the horrors of war and the morality and mentality of mankind engaged in mindless self-destruction. *Travels to Capillaria*, published several years later, is a scathing endictment of the man–woman relationship. In the midst of current feminist aspirations this Hungarian novel makes unusual reading, having as its central thesis the dominant role of women over oppressed men, both in marriage and in love–sex relationships outside marriage.

4

While he was writing his poems, short stories, novels, humorous sketches and *feuilletons* (the latter flowed from his pen at the rate of several per week and were generally mediocre), Karinthy began to feel increasingly alienated, and as a writer experienced a great sense of dissatisfaction. He was convinced that the time had come to produce the longest and most sustained work of his career. In the last years of his life he longed to produce a type of *New Encyclopaedia*, a latter-day version of the *Encyclopédie* of the French Enlightenment. Apart from an outline and a few brief, improvised sections, though, the projected masterpiece was left unfinished for at least three reasons. The hurried pace of Karinthy's work – the busy activity of a newspaperman driven by the need to make a living – was the main reason why the work was never completed. But even in the absence of such pressure, it is by no means certain that Karinthy would have written the *New Encyclopaedia* he planned. While his background in philosophy and the natural sciences would have been adequate for such an undertaking, he lacked the ability to organize such a lengthy and complex task. Although Karinthy had always wanted to be a philosopher (if only in the literary sense), his world view was too eclectic. In his conception of the world, the eighteenth century thinkers of the Enlightenment co-existed rather too peacably and improvidently with Nietzsche, Marx, and Freud.

But a further, more ominous factor also impeded progress on the work. As he deliberated on the projected œuvre, Karinthy's life took a decisive turn. On a chaotic weekday in March 1936, the writer was sitting in a café trying to work when he thought he heard "trains clattering in my brain". He thought he was hallucinating, but these symptoms not only recurred but were followed by others. After a time, a brain tumour was diagnosed.

In 1936, a brain tumour was more dangerous than today, and the percentage of successful operations much lower. As a result, few hospitals were able to hold out the prospect of a cure.

Karinthy's brain tumour was removed by the celebrated brain surgeon Olivecrona in Stockholm. The illness, the events leading up to the operation, the operation itself and its aftermath are described by Karinthy in *A Journey Round My Skull* – without doubt his finest and most lasting achievement.

5

What kind of a novel is *A Journey Round My Skull?* Is it a novel at all?

If we take the usual definitions into account, we would find it difficult to see this work as a novel at all, since it is entirely lacking in fictive elements. The author presents all the events from the first symptoms of illness to successful operation and recovery in the first person singular. Would it not be better to call the work a diary? A lengthy essay? A report? An autobiography?

To answer these questions we must assume a somewhat broader perspective. Karinthy aptly and accurately described the novelistic approach employed in his work. "I realized my only recourse was to observe and abide – without emotional commentary – all that was happening to me and around me. For once in my life I acted not out of respect for *truth,* which once pronounced is abolished and smashed along with the skull, but for the sake of *reality,* which is always and everywhere reality even when we are no longer invested with the power of expression." In keeping with his superior wit and irony, for a long time and in many of his works, Karinthy merely trifled with reality. But when reality shattered the fine toys of intellect, he was driven to submission, collapsing under the weight of a crippling illness.

The capacity for self-observation and introspection plays a considerable role in the creative style of every deliberate writer. One of the most deliberate writers in twentieth-century Hungarian literature, Karinthy was possessed of these abilities to an exceptional degree. We should also remember that Karinthy belonged to a group of turn-of-the-century, Budapest artist-intellectuals strongly influenced by the thinking of Freud (and also of Sándor Ferenczi, one of Freud's best-known disciples). A number of Karinthy's works show him contending with the teaching of Freud and Ferenczi. He was willing neither to accept nor reject Freudianism as a whole. His sovereign intellect produced a literary version of Freudianism which was both playful and deadly serious.

Karinthy observed that there were two elements simultaneously present in his subconscious: the Self *(Én)* and the Little Self *(Énke)*, the former serious and responsible, the latter playful and frivolous. The *Little Self* thinks along with the Self, but continually inhibits the Self from realizing serious aims and responsibilities. When the Self thinks sublime thoughts, the *Little Self* whispers obscene jokes. Whenever the Self conveys an observation or mood, the *Little Self* intervenes, the mood dissolves, and a new observation takes the place of the old.

This doubling of the self, inspired by Freudian mythology and expressed in terms of *Self* and *Little Self*, provided fertile material for Karinthy's greatest literary work, *A Journey Round My Skull.* The clash of two opposing tendencies operative in the author's subconscious charges the novel with its excitement. *Self* and *Little Self* are incompatible and irreconcilable; *Self* focuses all its attention on the subject, adopting a manner as exact, dry, and dispassionate as a scientific tract, *Little Self* avoids the subject, gives way to bemusement, and seizes every occasion and pretext to avoid the topic of mortal illness, going off on a variety of tangents instead.

To quote once more from Karinthy's aesthetic creed: "Whether viewed from the perspective of interpretation or that of composition, reality as *genre* has no need of the assistance of the so-called artist, if for no other reason than because in some inscrutable way which I am forced to acknowledge, reality itself does the composing. It composes and arranges, as does the writer himself."

A Journey Round My Skull is by no means flawless. Here as in other Karinthy works, some sections bear the traces of too much routine, of too light-handed a style. Nevertheless, one chapter of the book would have been enough to ensure the book its place in literature. The chapter in question is entitled "Avdeling 13". All of the preceding chapters seem to have been written as if in preparation for this impressive achievement.

"Avdeling 13" describes the operation itself. On one level Karinthy gives an exact account of the procedure, confirming his own observations with information subsequently obtained from his physician wife, who was present throughout the surgery. The next level isolates Karinthy's own thoughts and feelings. Each phase of the operation gives rise to the writer's reflections; and now, on the threshold of death, the duality of *Self* and *Little Self* has ceased. On a third level the chapter describes the relation between doctor and patient, from initial resistance to eventual alliance. One of the points of this rich and complex novel is that the writer – although taxed to the utmost – uses the very last reserves of his consciousness and will almost to "breathe" along with the doctor, thus helping in the operation.

And afterwards? What happened afterwards?

What happened is that Professor Olivecrona's 1001st operation was successful. Karinthy returned to Budapest triumphant and fully restored to health. His drive and energy were apparently still the same. He played cards and chess while writing the newspaper installments of *A Journey Round My Skull.* He kept Dr. Olivecrona posted on his physical well-being in letters written in German, soliciting medical advice on a variety of complaints. He personally sent the German translation of the novel to the Swedish professor. Then, a mere year and a half after the successful operation, during summer vacation in August, 1938, Karinthy suddenly fell ill. By the time members of his family and the doctors could reach him, they could do no more than certify that the writer had died. Apparently, he had suffered a stroke while bending down to tie his shoes.

He was buried in September in Budapest. By November, the Hungarian Chess Association had organized a master competition in his honour. The puckish spirit of the *Little Self* had come back from beyond the grave to preside over the players in merry triumph.

7

What are we obliged to confront in this necessarily brief study? The moral appended to the destiny of a great Hungarian twentieth-century writer certainly, but this in itself will not be enough for the inquiring English-speaking reader. He will want to turn to the text of *A Journey Round My Skull,* more eloquent than anything I could say here.

Karinthy was the lonely, latter-day successor to Voltaire and Swift, in accordance with his own inclination and the rules of those genres in which he worked. Had he been born an Englishman writing in English, he might have been another Orwell. But he lived in Hungary between the two world wars. He did what he had to, which for all intents and purposes meant that under the troubled circumstances of Hungarian literature he worked constantly, writing some very good pieces, and others which were less good. He produced only one masterpiece – the novel which the reader now holds before him, translated into English.

Such a realization – in literature – of objectivity truly reflected the philosophical depth for which Karinthy had always striven. From our perspective, his earlier work impresses us as having been merely a preparation for this devastating ordeal of self-reflection and introspection. Although his illness provided the opportunity, it was his unique talent which responded with the literary message, and the genre.

Mihály Sükösd

Contents

Contents

1

The Invisible Train

One afternoon—it must have been about March 10th —I was having tea at the Café Central on the Egyetemtér in Budapest. I had my usual table by the window, from which I look out on to the University Library and a bank. The only indication as to the bank is furnished by a plate bearing in big letters the words 'Mother Establishment', i.e. Head Office, and I have often amused myself wondering whether some gullible passer-by— especially one under the influence of strong family associations—might not misunderstand these words, and think of the bank as some kind of charitable institution where girls are trained for the sacred duty of motherhood. I, alas, know only too well that it is nothing of the kind. I lost my own mother at the age of six and that harsh stepmother, life, soon taught me to make a distinction between finance and the education of the masses.

While I have no exact recollection, I suspect that on that memorable afternoon I was more preoccupied by pecuniary considerations than by a desire to instruct the public. I fully recognize, however, that this last should be the chief concern of a man of letters. As a matter of fact, the two elements were combined in the present instance, as is often the case with a writer. Let me make my point clear. On the afternoon in question I was trying to decide which I should write first—my monograph on the role of modern man in society or a three-act play. In the end, I determined to write the play first, since I reckoned that the proceeds would ensure me leisure enough to write a monograph, even were it to be prepared more conscientiously and scrupulously than the average stage-play.

I felt relieved once I had made up my mind. Of course, the play, too, would involve a certain amount of preparatory work. There would be negotiations with the manager, a glance at some of the popular plays on in town, inquiries about the current season, and perhaps a chat with some of the actors. I felt, however, that my chance to become a dramatist was at hand, and I could ill brook delay. I had already decided to ring up D. when it occurred to me that Pirandello began his theatrical career at fifty-six, and nevertheless made a brilliant success of it. I hastily waved the page-boy back to his telephone box. If Pirandello could afford to wait till he was fifty-six, I should have time to finish the cross-word puzzle I had just embarked upon. Perhaps I should explain that for some years past I have made a practice of doing the cross-word in the only Hungarian newspaper which sets one regularly. This habit has grown on me to such an extent that, if I were to miss a puzzle, I should look upon the week concerned as an unlucky one. Nevertheless, these cross-words give me no end of trouble. The puzzle editor—whom I have not the pleasure of knowing personally—introduces every week into his clues 'down' and 'across' an aphorism which he describes as a 'familiar saying'. These are racy proverbs of the finest colloquial flavour. Their only drawback is the fact that they have no existence in reality. I am inclined to think that the gentleman responsible invents them himself and subsequently fathers them on to the man in the street, either out of modesty or artistic pride, after the manner of Kálmán Thály and his notorious 'eighteenth century' ballads. The reader will sympathize with any one who attempts to reconstruct an unknown proverb from the missing letters in a cross-word puzzle. I had even thought of writing to the editor or of accosting him in the street and demanding a confession of authorship.

In fact, I think it probable that some such idea must have been in my mind that afternoon, for I well remember how excited I became. The missing proverb read as follows: '..who.......romo.........ity ...lls.' I have no wish to burden this gentleman's conscience with the suggestion that his cross-word was the starting-point of my illness (as will appear later, it was of much earlier origin), but that he put me into a very bad temper is undeniable. What the devil did he mean by '..who.......romo.........ity ...lls'? There had never been such a saying. My struggles to complete the shady-looking proverb actually made me quite red in the face.

And at that very moment the trains started. Punctually to the minute, at ten past seven, I heard the first one.

I looked up in surprise to see what was happening. There was a distinct rumbling noise, followed by a slow, increasing reverberation, as when the wheels of an engine begin their unhurried movement, then work up a louder and louder roar as the train glides past us, only to fade gradually into silence, like the song of the Volga boatmen straining at their craft. I decided that it might have been a lorry, and returned to the mysterious proverb.

Only a minute had gone by when the next train started, to precisely the same rhythm—rumbling, reverberating and fading away.

I raised my head irritably towards the neighbouring street. What were they playing at? Trains running outside, or was it an experiment with some new means of locomotion? I remembered seeing the last train in the streets of Budapest when I was seven years old. It was drawn by a steam engine and ran along the Baross-ucca, where my home was. Since then, to the best of my knowledge, there have been only electric trams, and not even those in the Egyetem-ucca.

A few cars passed, but no other traffic. Three times I raised my head, and it was only when the fourth train

started that I realized I was suffering from an hallucination.

Never had I known one more vivid, so it is to be
understood that I did not at once recognize the hallucination for what it was. Since my childhood I had often
had the experience, when sitting at home or more com-
monly when idling along the street, of hearing some
one almost timidly whisper my name behind me.
'Frici!' It seems as though they were desperately trying to attract my attention, or still more as if the word
were spoken by some poor, shamefaced old acquaintance who dared not utter it aloud. The voice, too,
sounds familiar, though I cannot place it. I have the
feeling that it might belong to some forgotten figure of
my childhood, maybe a distant relative whom I thought
dead, but who in fact is still alive. It is as if he has crept
furtively out of a wretched hiding-place, and must at
all costs make me some urgent communication before
he vanishes again. At first, I would turn round on these
occasions, until I realized that my ear was playing tricks
on me. Then, as the incident never worried me at all, I
would walk on and take no notice. In time I even grew
fond of the mysterious voice.

This was something quite different. The roaring of
a train—loud, insistent, continuous. It was powerful
enough to drown real sounds. The waiter made some
remark, and I did not hear him. For the life of me I
could not imagine what was causing it. After a while
I realized to my astonishment that the outer world was

not responsible. In other words . . . the noise must be coming from inside my head. I experienced no other symptoms, and consequently did not find the incident at all alarming, but only very odd and unusual.

It appeared that I was the victim of an hallucination, but I at once concluded that I could not have gone mad for, in that event, I should be incapable of diagnosing my case.

Something else must be wrong. . . .

2

An Amateur Film Show

I dined at home with my son Cini. Since January I had been leading the life of a grass widower, as his mother was studying psycho-analysis and practising as a neurologist at the Wagner-Jauregg clinic in Vienna. Our conversation turned on geometry and physics, and I suggested the human body as an example of a machine. Cini was in Form V at the time, and had not yet tumbled to the fact that, in my explanations of life and nature, I used him like a scientist experimenting with a test rabbit. It amused me to try out my theories on him before any one else had heard of them. I would wait for a chance to introduce them during a conversation on school matters, as if we were talking casually about things he would learn in the upper forms. That evening he asked me about the mechanism of thought. I treated him to a discourse on 'engrams', the 'beaten tracks' of the mind, and conditioned reflexes, but as soon as the 'autonomous' functioning of the organs cropped up I turned the conversation towards my favourite hobby-horse, as if it had been a matter of general knowledge. According to my theory, each of the human organs possesses the elements of speech. I believe that the organs would be capable of 'talking' to us, if we could only understand their 'language'. Taking myself as an example, I began to put forward as facts a number of ideas which I could only *wish* were true. One of these was that, if I concentrate and observe myself closely, I can tell more or less from which part of my brain any given thought comes. When I count, make plays on words, or perform an analysis of any kind, something takes place behind my forehead. On the other hand, feelings, response to music, the passions (and *love*, I thought to myself, though this I did not mention) have their origin at the back of my brain. I determined to go on with my experiments in bed that evening. For years I have entertained a belief that, with practice, it would be possible to *direct* our thoughts at will and to move the ganglions from within, as an athlete controls his muscles or a pianist his fingers. Long ago, when struggling against insomnia, I evolved a theory on these lines. It occurred to me that I could send myself to sleep without using drugs, once I discovered the precise point in my imaginative apparatus —somewhere down in the region of the pituitary body —where the whole brain centre could be automatically anaesthetized and, as it were, prised up out of reality, with its workings stilled, much as Archimedes proposed to lever the globe. These fancies of mine had no interest for Cini. Instead, he began talking about water-polo and how he had been first in the high jump.

Modestly, but not without a touch of exaggeration, I recalled the athletic achievements of my own youth. (It is actually a piece of impertinence on my part to say that I spoke modestly. I remember the Hungarian writer Osváth asking a young poet, 'What have you got to be modest about?') Before we left the subject I told him that, with the exception of appendicitis, I had never suffered from an illness since recovering from scarlet fever as a child. I secretly counted upon this fact to impress Cini.

For a brief moment I remembered the trains I had heard that afternoon, but as speedily forgot them again.

Next morning they sent round at eight o'clock to see if some proofs were ready, and soon afterwards my secretary D. appeared. He informed me that the bureau I had bought so cheaply the day before needed veneering, and that it would be advisable for me to take the matter in hand, as otherwise I was going to be badly swindled. If I went to see the cabinet-maker myself he would do the job for half of what he was asking. Once in his shop I began chatting to him in an affable, condescending tone, using plenty of racy colloquialisms, as I always do when talking to men of simple education. It came as a pleasant surprise when he said something about my books, and so showed that he had 'recognized' me. This business settled, I dashed off a short article in the Café Bucsinszky, and by eleven o'clock was in my publisher's office, where I had to make arrangements for collecting a volume of my

17   B

short stories and giving them a title. I racked my brains
for quite a while, turning the proofs over and over in
my uncertainty as to which story I should choose for
the title piece. I had almost decided to use the sketch
entitled 'My Mother', when, for some reason unknown
to me, I selected a story called 'The Laughter of the
Sick', although I did not care for this as the title of a
book. It reminded me of Kosztolányi's early volume,
Sick Men. I remembered thinking when he published
it that a writer who had faith and progressive ideas
ought only to use robust-sounding words. The flimsy,
care-free impressionists of pre-war days seemed to me
on the wrong track when they boasted of their physical
ailments and claimed that art was largely a patho-
logical condition. On the contrary, it seemed to me
evidence of an exceptionally vigorous state of health.

On leaving my publisher's I called at the newspaper
office in quest of a subject to write up. In the waiting-
room I met B., who told me that it was time we got on
with that review of ours. If we started work in the
spring we should be able to put the finishing touches to
it by Christmas. Before I left I was handed a note from
a literary society, asking me to lecture to them. Good
Heavens, if only I could get all those unanswered letters off my conscience! For the present, this was out of
the question. There was that talk with the manager to
be arranged, then I had to call at the Ministry on
somebody's behalf, and after that I had to find a job
for my good maid Rózsi's husband.

I came home at two, and all through luncheon Cini

was worrying me about some party or other he wanted to go to. In vain. 'It's nothing for you, old man. . . .' After we had finished our meal I overheard Rózsi's little boy Pali, a young scamp in Grade I of the elementary school, reading aloud out of his ABC book. He had the typical accent of a peasant boy from the north of Hungary, but what he was saying made me prick up my ears. 'Little Isaac is reading. . . .' 'Little Solomon is writing. . . .' 'I say, Pali, just show me that book of yours!' I found myself looking at a clean, up-to-date ABC book, with numerous illustrations. But what in Heaven's name was this? Were my eyes playing tricks on me now, or had our educational authorities become so liberal all of a sudden without my hearing of it? One of the pictures showed a table laid for a meal and the family sitting round. Every one had a hat on his head. Underneath was a little verse entitled, 'Passover'. I began to wonder what kind of a book he had got hold of, and turning on a few pages, I saw that it was the reader of a Jewish denominational school. When I asked Rózsi, she merely shrugged her shoulders and said she knew nothing about it. At the beginning of the year she had sent Pali to the first school she came across. And a fine, clean school it turned out to be. The mistress was so kind, too. . . . Pali's reports were full of 'Excellents'. Now that she came to think of it, the Catholic boys did have a religious lesson to themselves. . . . By this time Cini was nearly rolling on the carpet with laughter. 'Well, Pali,' he cried, 'so they've gone and made a little Jew boy of you! From now on, we

must call you Ikey, and you'll have to grow ringlets.
. . .' At first Pali stubbornly defended himself, but he
soon changed his mind. 'I don't want to be a Jew boy!'
he yelled. Before long, however, he was playing quietly
on the divan, and when I came up to tickle him he
giggled and shouted, 'I say, you know, you mustn't
hurt a Jew boy!' I wonder who told him that one. . . .

Afterwards I dozed off for a moment. At four o'clock
I was to see a young author who wanted me to tell him
if he really had talent and whether it was worth while.
. . . I was going to tell him that he undoubtedly had
talent and that, for this very reason, he should leave
literature alone, as the age had no use for it. At five
o'clock I put off another job till the following morning,
and went out to an animal dealer's, where for months
I had been planning to buy an aquarium—or an 'anti-
quarium', as Erzsi called it. On the way I met that
excellent playwright, Laci Fodor, who began to talk to
me about spiritualism. I was interested to hear that one
of his plays was being filmed, and this reminded me
that I had promised an amateur film society to attend
a private performance at six o'clock, when there was
to be a projection of short reel films for Hungarian and
foreign members. I take a keen interest in this kind of
motion picture, which I consider has the best prospects
of developing into a genuinely individual art form and
of becoming, as it were, the music of the future. I was
given a warm welcome, and the performance began
immediately with the showing of some prize-winning

amateur films. They were fine, if unpretentious, examples of photography—an adventure on the Spanish coast, a little boy's morning walk in the woods and a symbolical rhapsody.

Then came something more interesting. A medical film, taken by an amateur, of Professor Cushing in his theatre at Boston operating on the brain for Jackson's epilepsy. In my youth I saw many operations performed, but never one like this. I therefore prepared to give it my closest attention. Only the patient's head was visible, as he lay strapped on the operating table. First, the surgeon went up to him and, with graceful gestures, removed the scalp, folding the skin back on itself. Then he worked round the skull with a circular saw, and lifted the detached bone off as if it had been a skull cap. Cleanly, almost appetizingly, he parted the cerebral membrane, which had a queer, unnatural look, like a hair net. Underneath it, one could see the grey matter of the brain trembling in its bony case. The surgeon stepped politely aside, so as not to stand in the way of the film operator, then faced the camera and smiled. I turned to my right-hand neighbour and began coolly to explain what was happening, but, in the middle of my sentence, I realized that I was talking to empty air. My neighbour, unable to stand any more of it, had tiptoed silently out of the dark hall. Even on the screen, the operation was rather nerve-wracking. All but five of us had failed to sit it out. I smiled with a feeling of conscious superiority. To be quite sincere, however, I had had my suspicions from the start that it was all a hoax. The figure that lay so still on the table could not possibly be a living man. The fact that hardly any blood was visible seemed to indicate that the surgeon was operating on a corpse for purposes of demonstration. If this were the case, it was still horrible enough. But I congratulated myself on having nerves and a stomach sufficiently tough for me to retain control of myself. I was once actually present at a mass execution by hanging. . . .

One of the five survivors (a psycho-analyst who happens to be a Karinthy fan) leant forward and reminded me in a whisper of an old theory of mine about the anatomy of the human intellect. In his opinion, the operation was only symbolical. I pointed out that it might one day become a practical possibility, but he answered that there was a slight contradiction here. The patient's sense of fear would have to be removed from his brain *before* ever he consented to have it opened. I appreciated the joke, but did not smile, for there had come into my mind the memory of my poor friend Havas, who died of a tumour on the brain at twenty-two. (This had been the first occasion on which I ever heard of such a thing.) I thought of his last days, his distorted features and the paralysed convulsions of his face when he tried to smile. A shiver ran down my back, as it had done then. What a fine, eager, ardent genius had been his! It was a curious thought that, in the grey matter of his brain, he had taken into darkness with him not only his own life, but the picture that same brain had formed of *me*, with such affection and understanding. Horrible, too, the idea that in his death something of me had died, and in a way so pitiable, so wretched. What was the use of believing in ourselves or in others if it all depended on that? I hastily reassured myself with the help of the safe hypothesis, inherited from my childhood and now hardened into a dogma, that, of course, such things could happen to others, but not to me.

At seven o'clock I was sitting in the same café as on the previous day, and, punctually to the minute, the train started again. . . . This time I did not turn towards the window, for I knew that my own tympanum was to blame.

When I look back to this particular afternoon in sorting out my memories, I ask myself how I can possibly have failed to connect what I saw in the film with the strange noises I had heard. As I now know, these were caused by inflammation of the auditory nerve, but it never occurred to me to see any relation between the two. I merely felt annoyed, and decided that there must be something wrong with my ears. No doubt they were blocked with wax. I disliked the idea, for I am a stickler for cleanliness, and as coquettish as a film actor or a young woman about certain parts of my body which nobody could call beautiful. I have the common sense, however, not to let this become obvious. When my intellectual self-consciousness protests against this tendency to regard the body as of equal importance with the soul in the struggle for existence, I still its qualms with the help of the following generalization. Throughout nature, I tell myself, every living body has two aspects—one connected with its private functions and individual life, and one which we may call the sexual. Each of our organs has likewise two aspects, adapted for completely different purposes. Thus, the eye is not merely an instrument of vision, but an alluring jewel, an ever-burning lamp, whose sparkle inflames the senses of the opposite sex. The ear is made not only that we may hear with it, but for our amorous dalliance as well. To a young lover, the mouth is not merely the upper opening of the intestine adapted for absorbing food, but the very kiss incarnate. It is in the case of the sexual organs that this fact is most obvious. For reasons of economy, they are associated, throughout the animal world, with those that dispose of the ultimate consequences of digestion. All my life I have tried to maintain this duality in my own nature. Notwithstanding my intellectual vanity (i.e. instinct of self-preservation), I have made room in myself for my physical vanity as well—a fragile ballast, all too easily wounded, and the cause of a vast amount of suffering.

Next morning I again postponed the work I should have begun on the previous day, and called to consult a well-known ear specialist at the clinic. The doctor, an attractive, modest young man, received me pleasantly. In his consulting-room we had a chat about scientific matters. Seeing that the subject appealed to me, he handed me a chapter of an interesting medical work he was writing. While still conversing affably he passed a long wire, wrapped in cotton wool, up my nose and through the Eustachian tube into my ear. I set my teeth so as to make no sound, and acted as if I had not noticed what he was doing. When he withdrew the wire, I went on with my unfinished sentence. In an off-hand tone he informed me that my duct was inflamed, and that this would fully account for the noises I had heard. I ended by telling him about a lady acquaintance of mine who was recommended by a doctor with a lisp to see an obstetrician (in Hungarian *szülész*). She understood him to say an ear specialist (*fülész*), and hastened to consult one. As a result, she was treated for a different complaint altogether, and the mistake cost her her life. My extempore anecdote gave the doctor a good laugh.

3

Some Short Weeks and One Long Moment

'To him who works, the days are short but life is long.' I remember how I liked this saying as a school-boy, though I always had an inkling that it was fallacious and, which was still worse, useless, even if turned the other way round. There is, however, something to be said for it. Being a kind of paradox or self-contradiction, it does set out to discover the truth on what my experience shows to be the right lines. If we would find the truth, we must start our investigation from the opposite side, for reality seems to be born of a conflict between opposing currents, positive and negative. I am quite sure, however, of one thing. Whilst I worked at high pressure and was constantly on the run during the last three weeks of March, my days were anything but short ones. I worried my head and argued over various problems, while all the time a feverish, exhausting animation seemed to sap my strength. An idea that there was something I ought to attend to was continually on my mind. All my life I have had this vague feeling that I have left something undone, or have for-

26

gotten something at home and ought to turn back for it. It seems that there is something I have omitted, and that the most important of all—perhaps the very object for which I came into the world. I had heard this peremptory summons many times, but never had it been so categorical or persistent. 'I ought to take a Ph.D.,' I said to myself ironically, for my friend Imre came into my mind. He had confessed one day that, at the turning-points of his stormy and adventurous career, he had always heard a voice saying that it might have been better after all if he had taken a Ph.D. when his parents wanted him to do so. But in my case, what was the mysterious something I had left undone? To look for it was like searching through a tangled cocoon for one thread which would unravel the whole. I kept reassuring myself by repeating that it came to the same thing in the end. If the chain were really there, I should set all its links in motion, no matter which one I laid hold of. This explained why I had written those innumerable articles instead of the one novel in a thousand volumes which I planned as a boy.

A poet friend of mine explained my predicament rather vaguely by saying that 'I was trying to find myself'. He may have been right. But if so, *who* is this self? Where shall I discover him amongst the many who cross my path, and by what sign shall he be known to me?

One morning, for no particular reason, I turned into the covered market and wandered down the avenues

27

of stalls, gazing at the piles of fruit and vegetables. Jars of pickled cucumber and sauerkraut flaunted their bright greens and yellows. Great piles of cheese suggested how delightful it would be to tunnel through the depths of them like a cheese mite. There were also catfish, split in half, their pink flesh showing against the wet slabs. In the past I had often looked upon myself as a kind of all-devouring spider, descended from my ancestor the single-celled amoeba, which assimilates everything that comes within reach. Now, oddly enough, I had no appetite, nor even my usual relish for a titbit here and there.

Next day I paid a visit to the slaughter-house, in the mistaken belief that I should write an article about it. An ox was about to be pole-axed. It slunk unwillingly along the wall, lowing softly, but offering no resistance. When the butcher stood up in front of it with his legs wide apart and raised the pole-axe, it lowered its eyes, as if ashamed of his intention. Quickly, however, it seemed to resign itself to fulfil the contract entered into with man. It had renounced the last years of life in return for spending the early ones, without a care or a struggle, on the sweet pastures. When the pole-axe fell it collapsed with a soft thud, like a row of coats from which the clothes-rail is withdrawn. I felt depressed on leaving and did not write the article, nor could I eat my lunch.

Instead I caught myself *revisiting* old acquaintances and places where I had never felt at my ease. I ordered a new suit and spent much longer than usual worrying

my tailor over the details, only to cancel the order afterwards and forfeit my deposit.

One morning, finding myself in the Kerepes Cemetery, I told the superintendent how much I was opposed
to the idea of cremation—the subject having cropped
up again in the Press. I explained that it seemed to me
an act of violence. A corpse may not be so *utterly* dead
a thing as we imagine. In any case, we cannot say with
certainty that we have no further use for it. I was not
thinking of material nature, or of the nitrogen required
by plants, but rather that one day we may learn it is
important for us and for our soul—or for the part of
ourselves which we call by that name—to disintegrate
precisely *thus*, slowly and in the normal way. May not
the astral body build up its own airy substance from
these remains? On my way home I felt ashamed of
these speculations. The fellow would look upon me now
as some sort of mystical occultist. Yet I only wanted him
to understand that all things have their due rhythm
and their own good time, which we have no business
to try to speed up.

And so the days passed. Sometimes I went to have
my ears attended to, as the trains continued to start in
my head, punctually at seven o'clock every evening.
I was getting used to the noise by now, and no longer
thought much about it. There were even days when it
rather amused me, and I was not at all alarmed by its
failure to disappear. The trains must have some destination, and one day they would reach it.

Some Short Weeks and One Long Moment

I was dining once at H.'s with an old friend of mine
—a fine poet and stylist—and an interesting nerve
specialist whom I met there for the first time. My
friend, a respectable bourgeois of fifty, had just fallen
in love. He sat in a mood of romantic silence and mystery, like any twenty-year-old youth. Even his face had
a younger look about it. After dinner, when A. and I
found ourselves together in the street, I began to speak
with a touch of envy about our friend and how he had
caused a sensation by his love affair. To my amazement
I heard that he was seriously ill with heart trouble.
This time I had not the idea which usually accompanied such news and which had occurred to me at the
amateur film show—namely, that a misfortune of this
kind could never happen to me.

I went with the doctor, who was also a psycho-
analyst, to a little tavern, where the two of us sat
talking over our red wine. The doctor had an interesting, eager mind, full of theories and ideas. With his
tall, well-built figure, large head, and round, childish
face, he reminded me of one of Thomas Mann's romantic heroes. He told me that once upon a time he had
studied my writings closely, as he found them an interesting subject for analysis and he had his own views in
regard to them. I thereupon told him all about my
comings and goings of the last few days and gave him
a kind of diary of what I had been doing, although my
nature is not one that looks back on what is *past*. To
this day I believe in man's unlimited potentialities and
I have no use for fatalism. The doctor smiled, shook his

head, and assured me that this had nothing to do with the question. He spoke of me as if I had been some old writer upon whom a final verdict could be passed by quoting his own words. I told him about the trains, and complained that recently I had often suffered from headaches. He was greatly interested, and put me some mysterious questions. Then he proceeded to diagnose my case after the fashion of psycho-analysts, with sudden, unexpected changes of subject, bringing the noises and the headaches into organic association with my character, desires, and disappointments, my memories of childhood, and a certain story about a muck-rake which I had written twenty years before. On the way home I felt thoroughly pleased with myself. There might be something in these psycho-analysts after all, I reflected, not without a tinge of remorse, remembering how often I had held them up to ridicule. That leaping about amongst associated ideas, however grotesque it might seem to the layman, was nothing more than an accurate and cautious medical report. This was the true science, and not that taught by the conservative school of medicine. A physician took only the patient's body into account. Yet, under the name of prognosis, he set out to foretell the *future* like any gipsy woman. Psycho-analysis never made this mistake, being concerned with the past and not with the future, although what was to come depended on the motives of the sub-conscious mind. To a thinking man, I reasoned, the body was of no significance, a mere rudimentary appendage or paltry raiment for the soul. . . .

Some Short Weeks and One Long Moment

As I sat in the café early next morning I was still
under the influence of this conversation. What he had
said about the impressions of childhood was perfectly
true, and there was something, too, in his theory of the
muck-rake. In fact, I was already feeling better for getting so much off my chest. The headaches would disappear nicely now. My physical ills, which were naturally the result of a mental condition, would vanish of
themselves as soon as I became conscious of their immediate origin. The whole trouble was mental. I had
only to be cured of that, and all would be well. It might
not be a bad idea to go and have myself analysed. 'Get
thee to a psycho-analyst, Ophelia!' the modern Hamlet
would say to his mistress. I felt my sense of humour
coming back to me, and this meant that I was my old
self again.

Then, all at once, a strange thing happened.

The mirror opposite me seemed to move. Not more
than an inch or two, then it hung still. In itself, this
would never have worried me. It might have been a
mere hallucination, like the roaring trains. But what
was happening now?

What was this—queer feeling—coming over me?
The queerest thing was that—I didn't know what was
queer. Perhaps there was nothing else queer about it.
Yet I was conscious of something I had never known
before, or rather I missed something I had been accustomed to since I was first conscious of being alive,
though I had never paid much heed to it. I had no

headache nor pain of any kind, I heard no trains, my heart was perfectly normal. And yet. . . .

And yet everything, myself included, seemed to have lost its grip on reality. The tables remained in their usual places, two men were just walking across the café, and in front of me I saw the familiar water-jug and match-box. Yet in some eerie and alarming way they had all become accidental, as if they happened to be where they were purely by chance, and might just as well be anywhere else. But—and this was the most incredible of all—I did not feel certain I was there myself, or that the man sitting there was I. There seemed no reason why the water-jug should not be sitting in my place on the seat, and I standing on the tray. And now the whole box of tricks was starting to roll about, as if the floor underneath it had given way. I wanted to cling on to something. But what was there to cling to? Not the table or the seat, for they, too, were rocking about like everything else. There wasn't a fixed point anywhere. . . . Unless, perhaps, I could find one in my own head. If I could catch hold of a single image or memory or association that would help me to recognize myself. Or even a word might do. 'There's something wrong,' I stammered convulsively. 'Ss-something—wr-wrong. . . .' And then I caught sight of my face in the mirror. It had gone as white as chalk. Good God, then . . . !

'A stroke!' The words flashed through my mind. I must have burst a blood vessel somewhere. At once came the realization that I had pictured it otherwise.

33   C

Some Short Weeks and One Long Moment

I had always heard and, parrot-like, had repeated that a sudden death was infinitely easier and better than a long, painful illness. One moment and all is over—as cleanly as a man shot down. I did not know what I was talking about. Although the sensation lasted only a moment, that moment seemed longer than my whole previous lifetime. I was still only half-way through it, and the agony of waiting for its second half seemed more ghastly than the suspense of a prisoner who is to die at dawn. Men are not good at measuring time. They have only one standard—their tempo of *experience*, as in Wells's *Time Machine*, where six months were compressed into a minute by manipulating the speed of impressions.

No one could possibly call such a death desirable, or prefer it to pain. Though I had no pain whatever, I felt that there could not be any torture in comparison with which it would not be worse. Outside, the sun was shining and I could see its light, but in my head everything suddenly went dark. I had only one idea now. By hook or by crook, I must hang on and keep above water during the second half of that moment. If I failed, the next instant would see me no longer captain of the ship. No more should I be in command of the myriads of tiny atoms, cells and organs over which I had been king since my birth. All that rebellious multitude, having shaken off my despotic rule, would become an inert mass again and would return to its effortless, natural position under the sway of gravity. In plain English, I should collapse on the floor. That miserable rag, my body, being only common matter, would soon adjust itself, but what was to become of me, the lost ruler of the empire? It was a ghastly moment—surely worse than the tortures of the Inquisition, I said to myself, as I began slowly to recover. This time it had not been a stroke, but I was the poorer by one more illusion. Never again should I long for a sudden death. . . .

The experience had been an appalling one. Yet, on thinking it over, I asked myself if this was only because I had no real faith to uphold me? I had had a ghastly, giddy sensation that it was only here, on *this* side, that I could keep my hold. If that began to give, I should be helpless. Never could I throw my line on to the farther shore. Out yonder I saw nothing. And yet this was not all. I felt that something else had let me down. Past and future, as I had imagined them, did not exist. Reality was *ever present*. The indivisible *moment* was reality—the one moment unique and *eternal*. The moment that *exists* could neither be long nor short—it was the only possible mode of being. And from this magic circle which is the prison of the moment no escape was possible. When it came the moment of my death would be as immediate as that in which I was now struggling to pull myself together. It, too, would occur in the *present* and not at some time in the future, as I had always assured myself for my greater peace of mind. The future, save as a figure of speech, did not *exist*.

The doctor whom I called to consult shortly afterwards did not even examine me. Before I could describe half my symptoms he lifted his hand. 'My dear fellow, you've neither aural catarrh nor have you had a stroke. And, for the time being, we needn't worry about your psycho-analyst friend either. Nicotine poisoning, that's what's the matter with you.' His orders were for me to leave off smoking at once.

4

The Ostrich Defends Itself

When I look back on this time from the vantage-point of to-day, my behaviour seems as strange and incomprehensible as it was during my first love affair at the age of twenty. Then as now, a kind of helpless inertia kept me turning round and round on myself. I did not realize that this Force, being stronger than I, was determining the path I should follow, as surely if I had been a pebble flung from a sling. On the first occasion life under the guise of the Great Instinct had been *attracting* me to itself. This time, as I now know, it was seeking to cast me off at a tangent into the outer darkness. But attraction and repulsion are governed by the same laws, and I, vain little planet that I was, once more imagined myself a comet free to follow what path it chose, independently of cosmic systems and obeying only some inner will of its own. I had fancied then that I could rush headlong into space and emerge victorious from the encounter. I thought now that I had only to hide my head in the sand for the Black Sun not to find me.

The Ostrich Defends Itself

Once, when I was thirteen, I swam the Danube near Szentendre. Darkness was coming on, and there was no one in sight along the banks. In mid-stream I felt my strength giving out. The current began to sweep me along faster than my weak arms. I saw that in a moment I would be carried several kilometres away from the island where I meant to land. For a second I was in an agony of fear. Gasping for breath, I began to tread water and waited for the pounding of my heart to quiet down. At that moment I heard something break into a howl behind me. A little dog had been following in my track—to this day I have no idea why. He, too, was at the end of his tether and looking up at me with frightened, despairing eyes. His appeal for help brought me to my senses again. I felt bitterly ashamed for whimpering like a poor, helpless little dog, and forced myself to start swimming again. After a tremendous effort I reached the island in safety. The little dog, too, managed to find a short cut to land, and he ran on in front of me, wagging his tail, when I set out to walk to the ferry. It was now almost dark. I whistled nonchalantly, as if to suggest to the dog that there had really been nothing in it. But I still felt a shiver down my back when I thought of the cold, indifferent water in which I had struggled for life.

On another occasion I went up one night in a ramshackle old aeroplane used for advertising purposes. As we were coming down flames suddenly appeared beneath the wings. I heard the pilot shouting behind me, but could not make out what he said. Thinking we had to jump for our lives, I began to unstrap myself. I distinctly remember that I had no sensation of fear. I had some sort of notion that it was quite an easy matter to jump three hundred feet or so, and that the most I could do would be to sprain my ankle. Meanwhile, however, we landed in safety. It turned out that my supposed flames were not flames at all. The pilot had merely lighted his magnesium flare to facilitate our landing.

The only consequence of this little adventure was a headache. I had no fear of death, as was the case when swimming. Yet it seems to have left quite as deep an impression on my mind, for on the many occasions when I dreamt of the earlier adventure during these weeks it was always in association with the second. I would dream that I was struggling in the cold, indifferent water. Everything was dark, and I could see neither the banks nor the little dog, but its howling followed me without intermission. I was desperately frightened—far more so than I had been in reality. And all at once I would be circling down in the little aeroplane, which had both its canvas wings on fire. At an incredible depth the landing ground yawned dimly under us like a black abyss. This time, in my dream, I knew that I was in mortal danger. A pallor of death would come over the pilot's yellow face, which seemed to leer at me. And still the howling of the little dog rang in my ears. . . .

In the daytime I felt no trace of the mood which

these dreams induced in me. I went on with my work, and used my spare time to make notes for a novel I had in mind, which was keeping me very busy. I wanted to write the tragedy of money, in the form of a subtle and curious tale. My everyday life went on much as before. I put off important business, as if I had eternity on my hands. I dreamt of the future like a boy who makes plans—if we may judge from all he proposes to do in his lifetime—not for sixty years, but for six thousand. I completely forgot the ox and what I had seen in the slaughter-house. My symptoms I continued to regard as unpleasant, but nothing more. I left off smoking, and felt completely reassured by my belief that the fainting fit which had so frightened me was due to nicotine poisoning. I was surprised to find that it was not difficult to give up the habit. After a few days the longing for a cigarette disappeared, and I could even work without smoking.

I saw now that my alarm over the first fainting fit had been worse than the fit itself. The fact of being afraid had frightened me still more. That was all there was to it. When I had a second fit of the same kind, immediately after an attack of giddiness, I took it far less seriously. In fact, I hailed it almost as an old friend. I knew that in a moment or two it would vanish without leaving a trace. And after all, nicotine poisoning was not a condition to be cured as quickly as all that. . . . I had read somewhere that the symptoms of it became intensified in the early stages of the cure, as in the acute phase of the illness. I looked upon the fainting

40

fits, like the roaring trains and the attacks of giddiness, as a part of my regular programme and therefore all in the day's work. The giddiness came on every evening at six o'clock. At first it was strange to feel everything dully swirling round in my head, but I soon grew accustomed to it. At seven o'clock the trains started, followed by a fresh attack of giddiness, and then by a fainting fit which lasted only a few moments. I would get ready to combat the fainting fits as soon as I felt them coming on. Those of my friends who happened to be with me on the first occasions when this occurred looked at me in amazement for a few days. Seeing that I went on chattering, arguing, and joking as usual and that there appeared to be nothing else the matter with me, they came to look upon it as a mere part of myself, not different in kind from any other bad habit. The fainting fits became so regular that I began to make a sign to Tibor the waiter—who was in the secret— whenever I felt the approach of one. He would stand discreetly behind me while I rose to my feet (at such moments I felt lighter than a balloon) and threw my head back. Then, seizing my waist and shoulder from behind, he would escort me without further ado to the exit. Once outside I would prop myself up against the wall. The days were still cool, and it did me good to be in the fresh air. If some one I knew happened to go by he would turn round in surprise. I would do my best to reassure him with an uncertain smile, or even exchange a word with him like one talking in a dream. Sometimes, I would give my autograph to little boys who recognized me. If I shook hands with some one, my gesture was like that of a beggar soliciting alms. After a while I would drag myself with infinite caution along a near-by street. Here there was a bench, on which I would sit until the fainting fit had passed. I knew by experience that it would not recur that day, and I could therefore go back to the café. My friends would still be sitting as I had left them, and when I came in they would stop talking for a moment. I always remembered at what point we had broken off our conversation, and it was I who took up the thread again.

And so still more days passed. Now that I look back at the titles in my note-book, I see nothing in the articles I wrote at this time which seems to throw any light on my case. I find titles like 'Dönczi Turi gets his own Back', 'Thoughts by the Way' (a light article, not a philosophical essay), and 'The Nineteenth Century' (not an historical outline, but a series of sketches). At the most I might have my suspicions about the title 'Fog', if this essay had not been a mere continuation of 'The Nineteenth Century'.

Meanwhile two new symptoms made their appearance. One of these seemed easy to connect with the other three (the trains, the attacks of giddiness, and the fainting fits). Immediately before the giddiness came on I had violent pains at the back of my head. These were so intense that for a moment or two I would hold my breath. I took them, however, for no more than a recurrence of an old complaint. As such I paid little heed to them beyond seeking to combat the pain with aspirin and pyramidon.

Early in April I had my first attack of retching. One morning (curiously enough on an empty stomach), a sudden feeling of nausea came over me, as if I had eaten some rich meal.

I was taken so much by surprise that at first I thought I must be mistaken. There was absolutely nothing wrong with my stomach. I tried the anti-insomnia dodge of fixing my mind on 'pleasant associations', in the hope that it would counteract the 'peristaltic convulsions' of my stomach. But the next minute I had jumped out of bed. Although I was still convinced that I should not be sick, I bent over the wash-basin with my mouth open and saliva running down my chin. The bathroom had begun to turn slowly round me, as if I were drunk. This, however, was far from being the case. I was most acutely alive to all that went on. After another moment my oesophagus began to throb in painful spasms, but this was only the hic-cups, and I lowered my head quietly until they had passed. The retching continued for much longer. To pass the time I tried to imagine what was taking place inside me. I pictured the alembic-like outline of my stomach painfully contracting, while my duodenum closed convulsively and allowed nothing to pass. The flow of regurgitated bile had ceased, and my stomach itself must be in a state of commotion. Unpleasant as the experience was, to me the most disagreeable feature was that I caught myself once more 'acting a part'. This is a tendency I had long ago observed in myself, and I have since constructed a whole theory out of it. According to this 'theatrical philosophy' I have outlined, nothing 'exists' as such, but all things act the part assigned to them—the apple-tree merely playing the part of an apple-tree, while the stars have their role in the great *ensemble* of heaven.

Incidentally, I have often noticed that my gestures are not original. I hold a cigarette exactly as my father did, and I have a way of turning my head that reminds me of a certain ex-Prime Minister of Hungary who once looked round in Parliament with an expression of surprise when some of us shouted a protest from the journalists' gallery. It is only when I am alone that I become conscious of these unnatural gestures, and once recognized I find them embarrassing. It amuses me to recall my first flight in an old-fashioned, pre-war aeroplane. I was alone with the pilot, who sat in front of me. Not a soul could see what I was doing, yet I found myself sitting in a rigidly conventional attitude. Carefully placing my hand in front of my mouth, I gave an embarrassed little cough. Then I tried to find the correct position for my hands. First I laid them carelessly on the sides of the 'plane, but I soon let them fall on to my lap and began strumming absent-mindedly with my fingers, as I had seen a fashionable actor do on the stage. And now again I caught sight of myself in the bathroom mirror. There I stood, waiting to vomit, with my legs slightly apart and turning a little to one side, as if

The Ostrich Defends Itself

I had to cut a good figure at all costs. My hand was raised to my forehead in a conventional attitude of suffering. The next minute I was retching my soul up. While the yellow bile issued in brief, violent spasms, I heard myself groaning as if I wanted to bring up my whole inside and have done with it, once and for all.

On waking next day I went through the same performance. I decided not to wait any longer before having myself examined. Being convinced that I was not really ill but merely had something wrong with my nerves, I called on Dr. H., fully prepared for the fray. He was an exceptionally talented, quick-witted man of very wide culture, with whom I had had many an argument on questions of religion and morality. This time he put on his most taciturn professional manner. After the usual questions, followed by percussion and blood-pressure tests, he sent me to get another ear specialist's report and meanwhile refused to make any comment. His air of mystery annoyed me. After all, I was the sufferer, not he. I felt it was his place to satisfy my legitimate curiosity, and not mine to bow to his 'professional' reticence. I let several days go by before consulting the ear specialist, and even then I did not take round his report. The new specialist was an interesting man personally, as handsome as a film actor, and he waved the first diagnosis disdainfully aside. There was no trace of catarrh, he assured me. A piano-tuner might well envy my hearing. Oh and by the way, why wasn't I at the rehearsal yesterday. . . ?

The Ostrich Defends Itself

There and then I decided, to my great satisfaction, that there was no point in going on. In future I should form my own diagnosis. I did not realize that I had long been weaving around myself a web of dissimulation—creating the peculiar frame of mind in which even sufferers from mental disease try to deny the existence of their symptoms (naturally, to themselves in the first place) rather than complain. I avoided all the good, straightforward, reliable doctors, for it annoyed me to find that they paid no attention to my 'interesting', or rather fantastic, theories. I sought out others with whom I could talk about exciting biological questions and who were prepared to follow me in my wildest flights. It flattered me to think that I interested them as a man more than as a patient. I found one or two amongst them whom I could control like mediums, so that they made precisely the statements I wanted them to. I would suggest to them what they were to say, and when they repeated these ideas I felt very proud of my sound medical instinct. And so I came gradually to the conclusion that my chronic nicotine poisoning was accompanied by a nervous affection of the stomach and that it would be a good thing for me to go to Carlsbad, if only this drudgery of writing would allow me the time and the money.

'Why d'you keep walking to the left?' Cini asked me one day as I was accompanying him to school.

'What d'you mean—to the left?'

'You're veering to the left all the time. It's a job

46

keeping in line with you. If you don't look out, you'll go into the wall.'

I happened to be reading Thomas Mann's great biblical trilogy, and as I was at that moment eagerly describing Jacob's adventures for Cini's benefit, I paid no heed to his warning.

That evening, with a sigh of satisfaction, I opened the book again. (I remember I had reached page 73 of the second volume.) After rubbing my eyes and polishing my glasses several times, I had to admit that I could no longer see to read properly, although the print was large. I resigned myself to the fact that I needed new glasses, and decided to call at the clinic next day.

As it happened, I did not go, after all. Instead, I had to inquire for a ticket at the Hungarian State Railway Office. My wife had written, complaining that she wanted to see Cini. If I did not bring him to Vienna that Sunday she would throw up her work and come home.

The letter ended with a grumble. 'By the way, what's the matter with you? I can't make out your writing. It's all dots and dashes, and the lines slope downwards. It doesn't look like your writing at all.'

5

A Meeting by a Death-bed

A sodden, grey, unfriendly morning greeted us when Cini and I stepped from the Árpád rail car into the dirty Vienna station. Every spring there are days of this kind. Nature seems in churlish mood, as if she has made up her mind that for once she is not going to respect the calendar. This year she will give summer a miss—the season on which she has hitherto lavished her gifts with so unstinting a hand. Year after year she splashes her green, red, and cobalt blue over the gigantic exhibition of fruit and bird and insect which she opens to the accompaniment of natural fireworks and a marvellously efficient central heating system. But the summer days have never paid back her outlay, nor made her an adequate return for her largess. This year she will have none of them, and turns back to winter. Shivering autumn is with us again, and a typical *autumn* mud squelches underfoot. A disagreeable *autumn* wind fusses angrily along the street, coughing and gasping like an old man.

No sooner had we alighted in front of our destination

48

in the Josefstadt, than the damp air had us coughing, too. A rickety Viennese taxi, with a high roof that made it look like a shabby old beau in a top hat, had conveyed us on creaking springs to my wife's temporary home with the H.s. Mrs. H., a lively, intelligent woman belonging to the circle of the Hungarian *émigrés*, had the intellectual distinction and learning which were typical of the book-loving Budapest society of the early nineteen-hundreds. Her husband—a brilliant doctor on the staff of Vienna's leading hospital for nervous diseases—had committed suicide a month before, during a mental breakdown, by tying a rope to the leg of a chair and strangling himself on the floor. Though I never knew him, I felt very sorry both for him and for his widow, as the marriage had been a love match.

We lunched off saddle of mutton at a typical little Viennese restaurant near by. I felt disposed to enjoy myself. It appeared that I was to have a talk recorded at the Vienna broadcasting station, and on Saturday I should be able to hear my own lecture in Budapest. I did mention casually that I had been suffering from severe headaches, but I was glad when nobody seemed to hear. An eager argument happened to spring up at that moment, in which every one wanted to express an opinion on a piece of scandal that was being retailed about two of our acquaintances.

After lunch Cini and I went for a walk along the Graben. It was his first visit to Vienna, and indeed the first time he had ever been out of Hungary. He was full of excitement, which he tried manfully to conceal. Like the real Fifth Form boy he was, he wanted to measure the height of the Stefanskirche by trigonometry. In a few minutes he had found his bearings. Soon he knew the lay-out of Vienna better than I did, and was discovering buildings of which he had never heard. He hunted about like a puppy in one of Jack London's novels, and remembered the events of his father's lifetime as well as those of his own. It came as an obvious disappointment to him when I had to pull up suddenly in the midst of our exciting voyage of discovery.

'What's the matter, Dad?'

'It's nothing, old man. I just want to rest a bit. Don't say anything to your mother about it. I've had these goes lately, but they don't last.'

Leaning against an advertisement kiosk, I took deep, regular breaths and struggled to keep off the fainting fit, as I hated the idea of making an exhibition of myself in the street. Fortunately, the attack soon passed off. I began to talk hurriedly of other things, and, much to Cini's delight, we were able to continue our journey of exploration through the Viennese jungle.

That evening we went to a cabaret where a show was being given under the title of *Sonia on the Plush Divan*. A clever Jewish girl, who had been thrown out of Hitler's Germany, was perseveringly eking out a living with the help of that harmonious something which was at once her life and her art. Everything around her was artificial and premeditated—the stuffy bar, the evil-smelling air, the uncomfortable chairs, the nauseating drinks, and execrable coffee. These she made use of in her art for the purpose of emphasis and local colour. Her partner, a tall man wearing a moustache, looked like a commercial traveller from the Levant. One could see from his face that he had earned his living in another way. To illustrate the text of the songs he showed a series of grotesque drawings in a magic lantern. One saw tears falling through the floor, a great weight being lifted from the hero's mind, and so on. For all its absurdity, it was a very clever show. There was a superior wit sparkling through it, together with a generous dose of vulgarity. Sonia was of the same type—a sickly, fragile little thing, with an almost transparent skin, slightly freckled, and great, brown eyes that shone curiously, like a lemur's. Working her arms grotesquely, as if they had been two red snakes, she began a curious dance, accompanied by a song about 'Ma-ma' and the 'dra-ma' of the seduced virgin. It was a brilliant performance, for she put her whole soul into it. The little minx deliberately insulted every instinct of her sex, yet through it all she remained unbelievably feminine. She danced serenely over the thousands of years of man's civilization, as if they didn't impress her in the least, for she, the eternal woman, went back a good many thousand years more. Why, she remembered the 'good old days' when they were that high. . . . There was something I found repulsive in her, and yet I caught myself envying the big, tough fellow who had caused the 'dra-ma' in the song by taking Sonia's place as the victim.

Next morning, as an old *habitué* of lunatic asylums, I accompanied my wife to the Wagner-Jauregg clinic. Though I did not confess it to her, I was impressed by the fact that she had a key giving her access to the locked wards. She put on a white coat and we closed the door behind us, turning the key. Two doctors said good morning to us, and I was pleased to hear that they knew my name. There was a certain stiffness in their behaviour, and a practised eye could tell at once from their movements that they were accustomed to being with the insane. We entered a neighbouring room, where some attendants were holding a half-naked man of immense physique bent forward on a chair. One of the doctors gave him an injection in the back from a long needle. The patient drew his neck away a little but made no sound. I had been the witness of an interesting new experiment. For several months a brilliant neurologist had been trying the effect of insulin as a cure for certain forms of mental disease.

My wife and I were alone when we entered the main ward. It was absolutely quiet as we went in. The 'restless' denizens of the ward were sitting about peacefully or lying in railed-off beds. A curious feeling came over me, which I had already experienced in the first room. I felt that it was all unreal. The people here were not living men, but figures of wax that somehow moved. Their mechanical gestures heightened the illusion.

A Meeting by a Death-bed

This was the exact opposite of Kaulbach's picture which had so frightened me as a child. There everything was weird, unpredictable, turbulent and menacing. Here every one who was not asleep was engaged in some monotonous, unbroken occupation. Their movements were as regular and predictable as the whir of a machine. In consequence, even those who shouted or barked like dogs were in no way alarming. You felt that they were merely doing their duty and acting a part for your benefit, like workers when the manager makes a tour of inspection. As soon as you closed the door behind you they would relax again.

In the first bed lay a slim, strikingly handsome young man with brown hair and flashing eyes. He had an exotic beauty like a bedouin sheik. I was shocked to hear that he had taken honours in his examination only a week before, and was now a qualified doctor. Three days previously, an attack of schizophrenia had brought the unfortunate young man, who came of an excellent Viennese family, to the asylum. I asked him what he was doing here and, shrugging his shoulders, he told me that he hadn't a notion what they wanted him for or why they were keeping him in a cage like a lost dog, when he wanted to get on with his work and open a consulting room. Or perhaps I didn't believe what he was saying? Well, would I please take a look at this? He suddenly shot out of bed like a panther and proudly tore open his night-shirt, revealing a naked body of superb proportions. Instinctively I had stepped back in alarm. My wife remained absolutely still, only nodding her head with the understanding of a practised doctor. As we moved on to the second bed I glanced back a little nervously. The 'medico' was sitting calmly on his bed again, absorbed in an attempt to catch his right thumb with the fingers of the same hand, exactly as one pictures the insane.

In the second bed was a smiling, red-faced old man with a white beard, who might have been an illustration to Tolstoy's story about the three foolish saints on the island. He was gazing round him with a serene, vacant expression, and he smiled benignly as he listened to the diagnosis of his case. '*Dementia senilis*, etc. In the habit of talking to God.' Suiting his action to the words, he immediately gave me a demonstration. I saw him assume a stiff attitude with his hands clasped as in prayer, whereupon he glanced up to Heaven and paused for a moment, as if listening. After a minute, he began to mumble, stopped again to listen and resumed his mumbling. He was answering the 'voice'. Now and again one could see him straining his ears to understand, and shortly afterwards nodding his head. He answered my questions without hesitation, in a trembling voice. Yes, thank you, he felt all right, but his hearing wasn't what it might be. Sometimes it was difficult to catch what God said to him, but He was good and didn't mind raising His voice a little. . . .

A murderer under observation came next. He had been on hunger strike for a fortnight and was being artificially fed. He drew away when one approached and his whole body quivered. He looked unconscious. It was obvious that one thought was uppermost in the ghastly inferno of his mind—he must not eat, he must not eat, he must die of hunger. Perhaps this self-imposed punishment might yet save him from the hand of human justice.

A six-year-old working-class boy. The nurse could not say for certain why he was there. Probably they had had no free bed in the proper ward, and in any case he was being taken back that afternoon. He was a bright but timid child, obviously not in the least perturbed by his surroundings. His whole attention was concentrated on a piece of rag tied into a knot as a plaything for him. Without taking his eyes off the ground he informed me in a decided tone that the rag was a mechanical rocking-horse and that they had lots like it at home. Why, the room was full of them. By the account he gave, his home must have been a peculiar place. The family spent their time drinking raspberry syrup and kept ice-cream in saucepans. Their furniture was made of chocolate and they changed it every day. I was told that he was incapable of telling the truth even by accident, and that if he talked in his sleep, it was to tell more lies. They had to keep an eye on him, too, because he had light fingers.

An uneasy feeling came over me suddenly, and I longed to get outside the place. I had often been in asylums before, but this was the first time I had ever felt afraid. I tried to discover the reason for my mood, and I found it in a fixed idea that had crept somehow into the back of my mind. I had the feeling that my wife was going to incite one of the patients to jump on to me from behind as a joke, with the idea of proving that I was really a little uncomfortable. I kept fancying that this was going to happen the next moment and that, once the madman had rushed at me, they would find it impossible to restrain him and the joke would end in disaster. Of course, the whole thing was pure imagination. Nevertheless, I breathed more freely when we were outside.

In the corridor there was a disagreeable atmosphere of desolation. Footsteps echoed mournfully up and down between bare walls that kept an aroma of carbolic. We passed through the neurological section, and for a moment I met the Director, Dr. Pötzl, a big man, who received me with extreme courtesy, talking in a gentle tone through slightly pursed-up lips. There were not many beds occupied in the sick-room. All the patients here were lying in a mood of apathy, and none of them seemed to take an interest in anything.

A case sheet over each bed gave a description of the patient. Its general appearance and Latin terminology reminded me of the tablets driven into the ground or affixed to cages for the identification of plants and animals in zoos and botanical gardens.

Here was a case of actinomycosis, which can certainly claim the honour of being a curious disease. A fungus contrives to enter the body; it resembles the tiny hooks on an ear of wheat in that it has the power of fastening itself so securely to the membrane of the throat that there is no dislodging it. Growing downwards, the fungus divides and a part goes to the brain, where it accumulates, causing the most extraordinary disturbances and eventually resulting in 'metastases'. The patient before me was an advanced case. His left leg hung out of the bed paralysed, he was as thin as a skeleton, one eye was gone, and his face was turned dully towards the floor, while saliva trickled from his trembling lips. He was moaning softly, complaining of unendurable pains, and imploring them to give him morphia.

The next case was more terrible still—*cisti cercus* or worm in the brain. A variety of worm makes its way into the central nervous system, settles there, and gives rise to cysts. The head comes to have the appearance of a rotten apple, wrinkled, flabby and prematurely old. A wet compress had been placed on the patient's forehead. His eyes were closed, but from his drawn mouth and nose I could see that he was not asleep. He was in pain.

The next freak was a case of acromegaly, or exaggerated growth. Exactly in the middle of the lower part of the brain there is a tiny gland known as the pituitary. One result of a disturbance in the normal functioning of this gland may be to provoke an intense activity in the cells, causing overgrowth of certain of the bones. This particular patient had a chin as large as a fair-sized loaf of bread, and in a few weeks one of his legs had grown to twice the size of the other. He listened attentively when I spoke to him, and looked at me with a

modest, respectful expression that contrasted strangely
with the arrogant expansiveness of his limbs.

My wife called back to me impatiently from the
door. I was standing before one of the beds, as if rooted
to the spot. I could hear my wife calling to me to hurry
up, or we would be late for our appointment with the
translator.

'What's the matter with this one?' I asked for the
third time.

'Never mind that! We've no time now. You can see
it's a bad case.'

'That's just it—I don't see. But he's got a queer
expression.'

'Well, he's what we call a "terminal" case. That
means he's only got a few days to live. It's an inoper-
able tumour on the brain. There's nothing to be done.'

'Why, of course. I remember now. My friend Havas
died of one—twenty-five years ago. So that's why he
looks as if. . . . Poor fellow!'

'Now, look here, how many times have I told you
not to show you're sorry for a patient? It isn't done.
You might be causing him no end of harm.'

'But I'm sure he doesn't know Hungarian. . . .'

'That makes no difference. They know from your
expression what you're saying, but they make out they
don't understand a word. You've got to be frightfully
careful. And now it's time we were going.'

She hurried in front of me down the broad staircase,
while I followed at a more leisurely pace. On the way

A Meeting by a Death-bed

I met a doctor I knew and we stood for a moment laughing and chatting together about Budapest. Suddenly, I broke off in the middle of my laugh. What was I thinking of a minute ago? What was it I had to be sure and not forget? I ought to have made a note of it.

Ah yes, I remembered now. The expression on the face of that patient in the third bed on the right. But who could it be? Whom did it remind me of? Whom or what?

'Hurry up there! What are you dawdling for?'

I was not merely dawdling. I had suddenly stopped dead in the gateway, like the ox I had seen unwilling to enter the slaughter-house. At that moment, it had flashed into my mind. I had remembered. The pale, vacant face of the dying man reminded me of my own expression as I had seen it lately in my mirror while shaving. I took two steps forward, then stopped again. With a foolish grimace, like a man who pretends to belittle some achievement he is boasting about, I said to my wife:

'Aranka, I've got a tumour on the brain.'

'You don't say so! A man of your age, too—you ought to be ashamed of yourself. You talk like a first-year medical student.'

6

The Eyes Give Warning

'What did you mean just now by saying that I talked like a first-year medical student?'

'Mean? Why, it's an idea as old as the hills! Every medical student imagines he's got all the diseases going. He gets small-pox and cholera and phthisis and cancer as soon as he comes across them in his text-book or sees them in the wards. "Professional hypochondria", we call it. It's quite the normal thing—but d'you suppose any one takes it seriously? I'm surprised you don't remember its effects yourself. After all, you spent six months as a medical student.'

'D'you mean to tell me . . . ? Well, let me tell *you* something. I'm not neurasthenic and I'm not twenty years old any longer. I've seen plenty of sickness and death in my time. And I've never been given to fancying things—least of all now. I tell you, I had a queer sort of notion that I'd seen that look before. . . .'

'Oh, you did, did you? Well, let me give you a little lesson for the future. There are three standard symptoms for diagnosing tumour on the brain—headaches, retching with giddiness and papillitis.'

The Eyes Give Warning

'Well, the headaches and the retching I've had already. Only I didn't want to say anything about it. And as for the pap—papil—— What did you call it?'

'Choked disk or inflammation of the papilla. The tumour presses on the brain in the line of least resistance. This causes blood to flow on to the membrane round the little aperture at the back of the eye, where it is detected by the ophthalmoscope. That's a sure sign —almost a *sine qua non*—of tumour on the brain. Not all cases of papillitis are caused by a tumour, but where there is a tumour it's always present. The four symptoms taken together are proof positive, like the four-cross Wassermann test for syphilis. And now it's time we were off. We're lunching with the G.s at half-past one. You won't forget those four things, will you?'

'No, no. Let me see. Headaches, giddiness. . . .'

'Oh, drop all that, won't you? You've got to speak to G. about the translation. Then you've to ring up J. and buy Cini a new pullover. After that——"

'I'm quite prepared to do the rest. But as to J. I've got my own views. You'll see, the whole business'll just. . . .'

Curiously enough, the scene in the hospital never recurred to my mind during the whole of that afternoon. Instead, I remembered that I had some urgent business waiting for me in Budapest. The consequence was that I determined to get home that evening, and home we went, although Cini would gladly have stayed on. I slept well, after a feeling of annoyance at my

61

inability to go on with Thomas Mann's novel, as I had
again forgotten my new glasses. Between sleeping and
waking I had voluptuous visions of some woman unknown to me, and next morning my mind kept no
memory of the unpleasant scenes of which I had been
a witness.

At ten o'clock I found myself on the doorstep of
the Mária-ucca eye hospital, and it was only at that
moment that I realized why I was there. Just look at
yourself! I said irritably. You're becoming a regular
old hypochondriac, the way you trot from one consulting-room to another. You're fussing about yourself
nowadays as much as F. and Gabi do. It's time you put
a stop to that. And then I smiled, for an idea had suddenly occurred to me. I would write a sketch in twenty
scenes on the 'Calvary and Ascension into Heaven of a
Patient Suffering from an Itch in the Ear', as he drags
himself wearily from specialist to specialist.

I was still playing with the idea when I reached the
first floor of the hospital. Little did I dream that *this
staircase was to be the last stage* of my childish life,
which I had thought would go on for six thousand years,
and that it was to ring down the curtain on my care-
free, arrogant existence.

In a corridor I met Dr. H., kind and obliging as ever.

'Well, well, it *is* a long time since we saw you! Just
come in! And what's the trouble to-day? New glasses
wanted, I suppose? *Anno domini* again?'

The Eyes Give Warning

'Yes, that's about it, Doctor. Another half diopter, I should say. You know what the man with long sight said. "If my arms were a bit longer, I shouldn't worry about my eyes."'

He began to examine the ophthalmoscope. In an off-hand tone, with the air of one who knows what he is talking about, I remarked: 'By the way, Doctor, would you mind having a look at the fundus, while you're about it? Just to see there's nothing wrong, you know what I mean. . . .'

'Of course. With the greatest of pleasure.'

I watched him take up a long, rectangular metal reflector. Placing this close to my face, he threw a brilliant beam of light into my pupil. As he bent close over me, I felt the ingenious little instrument brushing my nose and I could hear him draw his breath with a slight effort, as he strained to observe me closely. I waited for the usual reassurance. 'Nothing wrong there! You just want new glasses—a trifle stronger this time. Otherwise, you're as fit as a fiddle.' The reality was very different. I heard Dr. H. give a sudden whistle.

'My giddy aunt!'

The words were spoken without a trace of alarm. He was as pleasantly excited as an entomologist who has stumbled on some coveted specimen. For the one as for the other, the world held nothing but science and its academic delights. (I remembered the surgeon Dollinger exhibiting a cancer growth on a tray and exclaiming, 'Gentlemen, I ask you, isn't it a *beautiful* specimen?')

The Eyes Give Warning

'Well,' I inquired, 'what's the matter now?'

He laid down his instrument on the table and tilted his head on one side. I saw him look at me with a kind of grave amazement, as if I had suddenly become a stranger to him. It was the expression a judge might have when called upon in his official capacity to try a friend on some serious criminal charge.

'Why, your eye's full of blood at the back! There are spots this size. And the papilla's all swollen.'

I sat there, not knowing what to say. My imagination began to embroider on the theme of the criminal and the judge. And still I sat without saying a word, like a murderer discovered by the detective. For the life of me, I could not defend myself, though I felt certain I was innocent. So the back of my eye was full of blood! It was as if they said, 'I'm sorry, but there's blood on your pocket knife. Not a word from you, d'you hear? You just stay where you are and keep still! I'm calling the criminal investigation officers.'

And the fact of the matter was that Dr. H. jumped to his feet that instant and made for the door. In an incredibly short space of time the room was full. Assistants, house physicians, students, came pouring round, greedily snatching the ophthalmoscope from one another. As they fought over it a path suddenly opened through the midst of them. Who should it be but the dear old Professor himself? His tall, thin form advanced majestically across the room. Even he had been summoned to enjoy the fun.

The Eyes Give Warning

After a minute examination of my eye, he turned to Dr. H. I saw him nod approvingly, and his voice had an almost ritual sound.

'My congratulations! A really admirable diagnosis! It's a perfect example. I congratulate you.'

'Ah, Professor, I was lucky enough to qualify from your clinic!'

I felt it was my turn now.

'Gentlemen . . . !' I began modestly.

Every one swung round. It was as if they had only just realized that I was of the party, and not only my papilla, which had become the centre of interest. Dr. H.'s attitude changed at once. He gave me an encouraging glance, as though he had suddenly remembered that we had met before.

'Well, you see. . . . We can't say anything definite just yet. It might turn out to be anything. If you don't mind, we'll just go over to the next room for a moment. There are one or two little tests I'd like to perform—the field of vision, reaction to colours, scotoma, nystagmus. . . . Will you step this way?'

No one breathed a word now about my new glasses. In the next room I underwent a lengthy examination. Queer-looking instruments were brought to bear on me. Two bars set cross-wise, with four white points at their extremities, were rotated slowly and I had to say when the points came within my field of vision. With eyes screwed up, I watched the revolving bars intently, for I knew how much depended on my playing the game. Then came a rotating disk with red and blue

spots. They made complicated variations with it, and I
had to say when it was red and when white. And still
the tests went on. I saw them making notes and calculations. Several times the courteous, soft-voiced Dr. H.
passed his finger in front of my eye. I wondered whether
he was examining the pupil? Perhaps he suspected
syphilis. I realized with a shock that *I should be glad if
he suspected syphilis*—'only' syphilis. But it turned out
that he was merely testing the eyeball for possible oscil-
lation. At length I was asked to wait in the passage, and
half an hour later Dr. H. came out to me with a closed
envelope in his hand.

'Here', he said, 'is your report. You'd better take it
round to a hospital as soon as you can. I'd recommend
the Korányi. They'll tell you the rest, as you'll need a
lot more examining. Perhaps they'll send you from
there to another hospital. In any case, don't waste time.
I should go round to-morrow, if you can. And you'll let
us know, won't you? You can imagine how anxious
we'll be.'

'Thank you, thank you very much. It's awfully good
of you, I'm sure. There was just one thing I wanted
. . . oh, yes, I was just wondering . . . those drops of
blood . . . I suppose there couldn't be . . . a tumour
. . . on the brain . . . by any chance?'

He cut me short in a hurry.

'Well, you know, I did tell you it might be anything.
But there's no need to go imagining things. Besides, if
there were a tumour you'd have fits of giddiness and
retching and all sorts of special reflexes. Not a bit of it!

The Eyes Give Warning

I haven't seen you looking so well for ages. Well, you won't forget us, will you? And now I'm afraid I must run away. Good morning.'

Before reaching the bottom of the stairs I had opened the envelope. The report contained some data regarding the tests which I did not understand. At the bottom, in large letters, was the verdict: 'Choked disk, in the left eye one and a half, in the right two and a half diopters.'

I thrust the report back into its hastily torn envelope and walked slowly away. It was strange how light my feet felt. And everything, the street and all about me, seemed somehow different. But that wasn't it. What ought I to be doing now? I caught sight of my overcoat, and saw that it was getting shabby. Ah yes, of course— I had to buy a new one. Why, only the other day. . . . And yet. . . . Was it an overcoat I needed? No, no, this time *I had something else to think about, something quite different*. I remembered now.

Quarter of an hour later I was sitting in the library. I had sent for four books, two by foreign and two by Hungarian authors. In the index I turned up the following subjects: 'Tumours', 'The Human Brain', 'Headaches', and 'Somatic Changes in the Central Nervous System'. I was disappointed to find that the latest literature on these subjects was not available. Even the most recent books were two or three years old.

By about half-past one I had found the information

The Eyes Give Warning

I sought, and, as I put on my overcoat, I tried to summarize it for my own benefit. Stray sentences lingered in my mind. The following, for example. 'Sooner or later, these tumours inevitably prove fatal. Despite the hardly encouraging results obtained hitherto, an operation for the removal of the tumour is therefore strongly to be recommended, provided the diagnosis, and especially the X-ray, leaves no doubt as to its existence and location.' Another sentence ran: 'Hence, taking everything into account, the proportion of deaths resulting from the surgeon's intervention has unfortunately still to be reckoned as high as 75–85 per cent.'[1]

I wandered along the József-ucca until I found myself on the Ring. Where was it I had to go? Ah yes! Before lunch I had to run across to my newspaper office. Some proofs were waiting for me, and I had to sign a receipt. But why was I walking so slowly?

I ought to be hurrying now. There was something I had to go and see about . . . go and see about something . . . something very urgent. It couldn't be the hospital. I was going there to-morrow. No, that wasn't it. Wait a moment . . . it was something I had to talk over *with myself*. Something urgent that would brook no delay. Suddenly, in the depths of myself, I heard a mocking, insistent voice. I knew it instantly. The voice belonged to that cheeky little rascal who pries about inside me without ever asking my permission. It belonged to the

[1] For the benefit of my readers, I would again emphasize that I am speaking of books now several years old. To-day the position is happily more favourable.

The Eyes Give Warning

Little Me who sits inside the big one, 'now in my heart, now in my fingers, while sometimes he makes his pillow amongst the convolutions of my brain'. It was Little Me, whom I discovered in myself long ago and to whom I gave this name in a short story of my youth. At the big, decisive moments, like the one when I discovered life or fell in love or decided I believed in the other world, Little Me would begin to drum out a tune with his impudent, aggravating fingers: 'Well, what about it? Are you going to come to your senses at last? Aren't you going to give up those big ideas?' The same Little Me who will be sitting on the tip of my nose when the end comes, teasing and plaguing me with: 'Well, what about it now? Haven't you something to say at last? Or d'you still want to *put off* your confession —for the sake of a choice phrase or to get the last word in?' Little Me shifted his ground and I heard him ask, 'Well, what about it? D'you want to say something? I thought you wanted to say something. Get on with it, man! Or give a sign, can't you? Just be sincere about it—shout your hardest, man, yell the place down, out with your feelings! Why, you're afraid of being afraid!'

I did not yell the place down, but instead I just dawdled on. In front of an oculist's shop I stopped for a moment. The idea had long been in my mind—I couldn't explain why—to buy an hour-glass. I wanted a nice, slender one, with the ten-minute and five-minute divisions. And here they were—not at all dear, either.

69

The Eyes Give Warning

Yet I wandered on again without buying one. But what was coming over me? Why had everything become so unreal and accidental-looking? The houses and the shops—I had seen them a thousand times. What was I talking about—five thousand times. And perhaps this was to be. . . .

Every one has noticed that a town looks strange not only when one sees it for the *first*, but also when one walks through it for the *last* time, before leaving it never to return. I scrutinized the signboards as I passed them. The familiar shop-windows were as painfully new, and the whole place had the same appearance of having shrunk and dwindled as when we first catch sight of the house and the courtyard and the garden where we spent our childhood. We can hardly believe our eyes, so much larger and more imposing had we expected to find them. Yet what hurts us when we return as grown-ups is not the thought of how beautiful and precious was all we have lost, but the realization of how trivial and insignificant was the childhood on which for a lifetime we have nourished our recollection.

Mr. Láng, the secretary, smiling as usual, ushered me in. I pulled myself together and managed to exchange a joke with Panni. R. Sz. came in, with his affable 'beyond good and evil' expression, that contrasts so strangely with a wild crop of hair like a revolutionary's. I like him because he is interested in scientific matters and not only in the humanities, as most

70

young writers are apt to be. We started to talk about
the new medical discoveries and developments which
were tending to widen the sphere of operations, for, if
the campaign against disease was gaining strength, the
diseases were arming, too.

'For example, there's my case,' I interposed. 'I've
got a tumour on the brain.'

He positively roared with laughter.

'And you call yourself an educated man! My dear
fellow, have you any idea what you're talking about?'

'I most certainly have.'

'Ah ha, I think I see now. Why, yes, of course! If
you're ill, it's got to be something special. The common
or garden won't do, eh? Well, old man, you've gone a
bit too far this time. Take my advice and say something
that sounds just as good and isn't so dangerous. Tell
people you've got extrasystole and dyshidrosis.'

'I tell you, my trouble is just a tumour on the brain.'

'Well, look here, we'll come back to this argument
some other time. For instance, when you can show me
a certificate proving that you've got a choked disk in
the eye.'

My hand shot into my pocket.

'Perhaps this'll interest you.'

He glanced through the report, then started to read
it a second time, looking carefully at the name in which
the report was made out. I was the only one who saw
that his face turned a shade paler. For an instant I felt
decidedly proud of myself. But the feeling did not last.
I saw him fold up the report.

71

'Well,' he said, a little uneasily, 'that's a bit of all right, eh? A real—bit of—all right. Er . . . you'd better take this back.' He glanced suddenly at his watch. 'My, I've got to dictate an article! Better be going. So long, everybody!'

As soon as he had gone I sat down on the sofa and crossed my legs, as the floor had started to roll about oddly under my feet. I felt like a man hanging over a precipice when he suddenly realizes that the others want to let him drop.

7

The Ghost Train

Last year they built a new-fangled type of scenic railway close beside the old one in the Budapest Amusement Park. On the older railway dwarfs and princesses, idyllic scenes and palaces of crystal greeted the traveller at every turn. The new entertainment, if I remember rightly, was called 'The Ghost Train'. Immediately after the start one was in pitch darkness with an ominous wind howling about one's ears. Invisible doors slammed, chains rattled, and the air was full of sighing and lamentations, as in that 'outer darkness' of which the Bible speaks. A sickly light glimmered for an instant against the wall, barely long enough to reveal the presence of a skeleton, for the ghost train had already hurtled past as if on its way to the nether regions. One's seat tossed and pitched from side to side. In the next section a man was lying who had apparently committed suicide. He was succeeded by one hanging on a gallows and then by a man buried alive, who was struggling to open the lid of his coffin. Screech-owls hooted and birds of ill omen croaked dismally. It was a queer

form of entertainment for the light-hearted public. Yet
an entertainment it undoubtedly was, to judge from
the complacent laughter of the passengers as they jokingly tried to frighten one another, shrieking and yel-
ling with delight. Experience showed that they were
right to let out their feelings. For those who sat quietly
in the darkness it was harder to endure the crude, sick-
ening atmosphere of nightmare and panic, with its
accompaniment of a doleful, braying hurdy-gurdy.

I did not turn up at the hospital next day, nor did I
write to Vienna. I put off doing either, so that I could
wait for the time being and watch quietly in the dark.
If I did this I felt that perhaps I might discover a doorway leading to the exit or even one opening on to a final
solution of my problem. I persuaded myself that nothing was so important for me as to keep quiet, and
moreover I had a great deal to do. This state of mind
tended to create for me a dream-like world of my own,
and as such did me no harm in itself. But it did not
last long.

Tell-tale flashes of lightning began to alternate with
the braying of the hurdy-gurdy. If a man cuts his finger
in the morning he will be sure to notice during the day
that he is everlastingly knocking that particular finger.
The idea is probably a mistaken one, for he knocks it
every day as often without realizing it. Before my illness I had many a time glanced through the pages of
Bing's *Neurology* and Bleuer's *Psychiatry*, but now
that the print ran together before my eyes it was the

illustrations which seemed to come suddenly to life. Those pottering, palsied paralytics were soon as familiar to me as old friends. There were sufferers from myxoedema with their characteristic flabby expression, megalomaniacs with chins thrust arrogantly forward, and a microcephalous boy with a tiny head and a smile on his broad face that was Homeric rather than Dantean in its infernal gaiety. There was one photograph to which I returned again and again. It represented an idiot woman, stark naked and wasted to the bone. She was leaning against a hospital bench, and her profile, with the high, concave forehead and bedraggled hair, hinted at a secret agony she could never express, even if she were to moan like an animal. There was also a boy with Little's disease. He was crawling on all fours, with his limbs grotesquely contracted. The damage had been done to his brain at birth, when his soft skull had been crushed by the matrix. In some of the photographs a square black mask had been placed over the patient's eyes to prevent identification.

That evening as I lay with the lamp-shade tilted towards my bed, a sudden longing came over me to think of something else at last. How good it would be to look once more down the corridors of thousands of years to the violet horizon! Unable to read myself, I had an inspiration. I called the maid Rózsi, and for hours the good soul read aloud to me from the story of Joseph. In a slightly sing-song voice but with extraordinary understanding, she rolled off the heavy, involved sentences of Thomas Mann. When I asked her how much she understood of a text that gave the most learned a good deal of trouble, she shrugged her shoulders and hastened to assure me that she understood very well, for this book contained nothing she had not already learnt in the religious lesson at school. We had, in fact, reached a memorable chapter. The brothers, exasperated by Joseph's manner of life, by his happiness and overweening presumption, waylay the youth, resplendent in his coat of many colours, beat him soundly and fling him into a dry well. Here he lies bound and bleeding, with broken ribs and eyes half gouged out. His situation appears hopeless. In this plight he falls to thinking of his previous life, spent gaily in the full blaze of the sun. How carelessly he had taken it all for granted! With no prospect of ever being able to apply it in practice, he draws a moral from his reflections: those whom we think are our devoted servants, prepared for any sacrifice on our behalf, merely because they admire us and sing our praises, cannot help us in misfortune because the least and most wretched amongst them, for all his enthusiasm, *loves himself better than he loves us.*

I hurriedly stopped Rózsi in her reading and tried to sleep.

Next morning, as I strolled through the centre of the town, I came upon a crowd gathered in the street. An epileptic workman lay writhing on the pavement. A glance showed me that he was not shamming. Froth had broken out on his lips and the whites of his eyes were turned up. Jackson's epilepsy, I said to myself as I turned away. I knew now how to distinguish it from the genuine thing. I also remembered that they had tried to cure this, too, by surgery; the skull had to be lifted in order to relieve the pressure on the brain. They had had good results, too—*when there was no tumour.*

I started suddenly, realizing that I had knocked into a blind beggar, as he stood tapping with his stick for some one to lead him across the road.

I had felt uneasy ever since the scene in the newspaper office. I bitterly regretted having given away the contents of my report for the sake of scoring a hit. I should have done much better to wait a while. How many times had I noticed that he who boasts too soon is in for a fall? And yet—perhaps it might still be possible to make them forget all about it. There was even a chance that no real harm had been done and that the whole bad dream would disappear of itself.

But it was already too late. My suspicion that now every one knew everything proved to be justified.

At first I tried to convince myself it was my imagination that made me think people were turning round hurriedly as I passed. Acquaintances whom I met scrutinized my face with inquisitive expressions. They made room for me to pass in front of them and ran up to help me on with my overcoat. I sensed an atmosphere of expectant curiosity about me. I tried to reassure myself by saying that it was nothing after all, and I was exaggeratedly, almost aggressively, light-hearted.

For several days I never went to the newspaper office. I preferred to idle along the streets, though here I was constantly meeting sick people. A mood of animosity came over me by degrees. With this went an idea that pursued me like the wail of a hurdy-gurdy in the street, ever more plaintive, ever more insistent, now following close behind me, now turning after me at the corner—an odd sensation that *I was living here as a guest.* Driven on by wild envy, I seemed to pace the streets of a foreign town, where all about me men watched and waited.

In the Egyetem-tér I met D., whom I had not seen for a long time. After we had said good-bye, he turned back and remarked casually, 'Oh, by the way, I hear there's been something wrong with you lately. Kidney trouble or something, wasn't it?'

I hastily interrupted him.

'Don't you believe it! I just had a touch of neuralgia.'

'Oh, that was the trouble, was it? Well, if I were you, I'd just look in at the hospital in the M.-út. I spoke to Dr. R. about you. You won't forget, will you?'

'What d'you say? You've told him about me?'

Other people who usually passed me in the street now stopped for a chat, although they never had anything to say. It was now impossible for me not to realize that they were scrutinizing my face. In the tram one day a man younger than myself stood up and insisted on my taking his seat. Oh, but it didn't matter in the least that I hadn't remembered him, as he knew *me* quite well by sight. And he did not take his eyes off me for a second until he sat down again.

It had been a mistake to let any one know, a big mistake. This was intolerable. I caught myself turning my head nervously, for all about me I felt they were talking, gossiping, prognosticating. And somewhere there was a Somebody—I could not imagine who it might be—gathering up the threads, observing, biding his time, telephoning, making arrangements, watching for the psychological moment. An unknown Porfir whose attention Raskolnikov had had the supreme misfortune to draw upon himself.

I felt I must do something to banish this suspicion that others were acting instead of me. I ought to take some definite step myself, though I would gladly have rotted away in some dark corner, where I should never have to think of anything any more.

It was the charming, absent-minded, meditative Gyula whom I decided to consult, for he was the best and the most sceptical of my doctor friends. We had never previously discussed scientific matters, as he happens to be interested in the finer sorts of literature. He received me with so delightful a freedom from preconceived ideas that I was convinced he knew nothing about me. He would surely have said so, had he heard. Instead, we started joking together and his wife Elza came in. I tried to amuse her, but was disappointed when she hardly said a word.

'I say, Gyula,' I began, 'you might just look at my stomach and lungs, would you, and test a few of my reflexes? I've had a lot of headache lately, although I knocked off smoking a fortnight ago. And what d'you think about my eyes?'

'Yes, I know . . . I mean . . . you mentioned something about that. I'm glad you've reminded me of it. I was thinking you ought to go round to the hospital in the M.-út—Professor R.'s expecting you, incidentally. If you like, I can ring him up now.'

For a moment I said nothing.

'If he's expecting me, you needn't trouble. I'll go.'

The children followed me into the hall. I stood chattering away eagerly to them, but all the time I was wondering when I could have mentioned that eye business to Gyula. No, I was quite certain. I had never breathed a word of it.

At lunch time Dénes unexpectedly informed me that my insurance policy was running out and that he must have the money at once for the next premium, as it would be a pity to lose the benefit of all those I had paid.

Five o'clock found me sitting in Prof. R.'s consulting-room in the Falk Miksa-ucca. He turned out to be calm, self-possessed, smooth-faced, and I should have taken him for the chairman of some successful company had I not known that he was an eminent medical man.

80

The Ghost Train

Only his reserved manner suggested the scientific expert. He did not allude to the fact that he had been told I was coming, but asked me at once to strip and began a lengthy examination. He tested a dozen or so of my reflexes, probed me with his finger, tickled me, made me walk, and raised my arms and legs. With a heart that beat ever more calmly and a returning self-confidence, I heard him murmur, 'Negative . . . negative.' Of course, they were negative. I could have told him that. Let him just see me walking with my eyes closed! Why, there was nothing in that. . . .

I suddenly remembered that another friend of mine named Gyula, Dr. B., had taken an X-ray of my skull in his laboratory, and I hastened to mention the fact.

'I know,' he nodded. 'The photographs are here.'

'You say you've got them here . . . ? Well, was there anything in the brain?'

'Nothing. But we must have another look.'

'But, if there was nothing, what's the use of looking again? And, if I'm not mistaken, all my reflexes are negative, except for the papilla. . . .'

'Yes, yes, of course.'

'So there's nothing definite at all—?'

'Just a little dysmetria to be cleared up. I'll think it over. In any case, please look in again to-morrow.'

I made up my mind not to look in again to-morrow, whatever happened. I did not like the man, and I had the feeling that he did not like me. The others were so charming and always ready for a joke. They took me into their confidence, and were as pleased as I was when a test proved negative. Instead of just going on, they would welcome it as a success for me. This fellow would be downright glad if there were something wrong, and I felt that he would never rest till he had found something. He was only interested in positive results. In fact, he had a prejudice in favour of disease as opposed to health. And he didn't like me. He felt that I needed men of the instinctive type around me, and he wanted to keep them away. He was the kind who would insist on opening the window when one could see quite well without it; he hadn't learnt that too much light renders the eyes as helpless as total darkness.

Next morning, in the Café Bucsinszky, I saw my friend the novelist Lajos Nagy looking at me in surprise as I came back from the telephone box.

'Couldn't you get on?'

'There wasn't anybody there.'

'But the phone never rang!'

'Of course, it did. D'you mean to say you never heard it?'

'I never heard anything.'

'Why, yes. I believe you're right! It was I who meant to ring up the other Gyula. I don't know where I got the idea that I was wanted urgently. I thought I heard the phone ringing. . . .'

'That you, Gyula?'

'Speaking.'

'I say, I hear those X-rays of my head are ready.'

'That's right.'

'And that there's no sign of anything in the brain.'

There was a pause so brief that I hardly noticed it.

'No, that's right.'

It was my turn to pause now. Then I added in a joking tone, as if I were putting him one of the riddles we both enjoy: 'Gyula, I'd like to ask you something.'

'Go ahead.'

'If there was anything in my brain, would you tell me?'

Another pause. 'No.'

'Why not?'

'Because up to a certain point the doctor is bound to secrecy in talking to a patient.'

I laughed.

'Gyula,' I said, 'don't you think your second answer throws some doubt on the value of your first?'

'I'm afraid it does.'

'Well, what am I to think now?'

'I really don't know.'

'All right, we'll talk it over again. Thanks very much. Good-bye.'

Next morning, accompanied by my secretary, I went to the Korányi Hospital and was registered as a patient. While they were taking down particulars in the office, Dénes remarked jokingly that my behaviour was like that of a man who, after long struggles and hesitation, had decided to give himself up to the police.

8

A Gesture in the Window-Pane

I should not like the reader to believe that, in thus harping on the police and criminal theme, I am merely striving after a cheap metaphor or using stage effects to show myself off in a more interesting light. I am particularly anxious to avoid 'symbolical' writing. It is far more important to me than it can be to the reader that I should relate *what happened* in a sober, clear style, undistorted by my present frame of mind. If only for this reason I could not do otherwise than put on record the fact that, throughout my illness, I was the victim of a *sense of guilt* which has only now reached the threshold of consciousness. I had the feeling that I was guilty of some forgotten sin that had never been condoned because the memory of it remained outside my conscious mind. This perhaps explains why, from first to last, I was incapable of complaining or rebelling against my fate. As for the metaphor I use, any reader who brings enough sympathy and understanding to bear on *himself* will agree with me that every day there occur three or four tiny incidents that throw light not only

84

on that day, but on our whole destiny and spiritual development up to the time in question. All we have to do is to read their message.

Let us take an example. It has only just occurred to me that the medical examination and confinement in hospital of a patient before he is treated exactly correspond to the detention of an accused man before trial. The accused has only one idea in his head—namely, is he going to be declared guilty and, if so, what will his sentence be? Whichever way the verdict runs, he is bound to suffer a certain punishment from the fact that he has publicly come under suspicion.

When I reached the hospital next morning I had to undress at once and get into bed. Whether I felt ill or well was beside the point—the rule had to be observed. As I lay waiting for the first doctor to come round I asked for the papers, but I found it impossible to read. A kind-hearted nurse at once undertook to read aloud to me, without even asking what was the matter. I pretended I was interested in the leading article or the short story, but I soon turned on a page or two with her to the gossip column. I had begun to heave a sigh of relief when I realized that there was to be no mercy shown me. The very first paragraph, with its small print and laconic wording, informed me that I had been tracked down. They were sorry to hear that, as the result of a slight illness, I had entered one of the leading Budapest hospitals of my own free will for the purpose of being overhauled. They looked forward to hearing in a short time, etc., etc. I resigned myself to wait for the consequences, but half an hour later my vanity was wounded by the information that no one had rung up to inquire after me. This brought Vienna to my mind and I hastily telegraphed, 'Press reports incorrect. All well. Letter follows.'

At ten o'clock, the preliminary overhaul began. I soon made friends with Dr. Cs., who turned out to be a chatty, amusing, good-humoured man. I described my reflexes to him in advance, for I have had plenty of practice in extending my arms and in bending backwards and forwards with my eyes closed. When somebody tickles the sole of my foot I move my toes like an adult, and not like a baby or an ape. 'That'll do,' said the doctor. Next day they would test my blood for sugar and so on—just a little prick, you know. And meanwhile would I care for a game of chess? I was deligl.ted to accept his suggestion and we arranged to meet after lunch. I had heard that he was a very fine player.

Well, it looked as if this hospital wasn't going to be such a bad substitute for my café, after all. The load I had felt on my mind that morning began to lift. As it turned out, I lost the game of chess after lunch, but my good spirits were kept up by the news that some cheery friends had telephoned to say they would call on me later. During the afternoon the sun came out. A feeling of calm and well-being took possession of me which I could not at first explain. I thought it might be due to my having no need to work and therefore a ready pretext for idleness. But this explanation was too superficial. There was something in my mood which I had never known before. For the first time I found myself in the happy position of being *utterly free from responsibilities.* How am I to explain this to the average reader, accustomed to an orderly, average way of life? A tempestuous soul like mine is tossed and buffeted about in an everlasting state of tension, the like of which you happy ones know perhaps once or twice in a lifetime. Every minute I am obliged to concentrate on my *whole life.* To me each minute is as it would be to you if you were to jump out of a sixth-floor window or to be caught up in a hurricane. A foolish sensitiveness indeed—but how am I to be cured of it? Or perhaps it is no more than an excess of timidity inherited from childhood's dread of punishment and the big stick. As Shakespeare says: 'Cowards die many times before their deaths; The valiant never taste of death but once.' And now it looked as if I were going to be cured, after all. I felt absolutely at peace. This was no longer my whole life; it was just one afternoon. It might be that I was very ill. Perhaps I was even going to die. Yet this had nothing to do with that afternoon, nor I with the man born to sorrow from the day he came into the world. I went on weaving a silent pattern out of my thoughts— and yet they were not so much thoughts as stray words, for I did not wait till the maze of logic brought forth its fruit. No sooner had the flowers opened than I gathered them, even if they were only flowers of speech. In this way I composed two excellent epigrams for the other Gyula. I felt that anything might still happen. The overhaul might disclose any one of a hundred things.

A Gesture in the Window-Pane

Whatever the outcome, I should still have plenty of time to think things over and make my final decisions.

By the evening my mood had clouded over a little. It was not the giddiness and the headache that depressed me—by eight o'clock they were generally over and done with. The strange silence, however, was something I had not been prepared for. After seven o'clock the swift footsteps in the corridors were hushed and the doctors went home or withdrew to their rooms. The wide, barrack-like passages were deserted and an eerie blue light gleamed in the wards. I, too, put on the blue lamp in my room and sat gazing out at the wet gardens —for in the meantime it had started to rain. I turned the whole question over in my mind, wondering if I really had anything to lose. All other considerations apart, I felt certain that *not being* would prove exceedingly monotonous, as compared with the gay variety of life. On the other hand, nothingness undoubtedly had its points. There would be no need to carry on conversations or to search for excuses. If only man could enjoy its advantages in some *third state* beyond life and death! If only I could go into my favourite café and yet not be there—could sit down in the midst of the people and have none aware of me! Suppose it really was as I had imagined it in my book *News from Heaven*—or had I been mistaken, after all?

I began to creep on tiptoe down the blue-lighted wards, as if I were looking for some one. The nurses watched me go by without saying a word. Most of the patients were lying quietly on their backs, but not sleeping. I discovered one room full of children who were being looked after while their parents went to the theatre or dined out. With wide-open eyes, they lay dreaming about life. In one bed a man was whistling softly. It was my friend Otto Ernst, the adventure-loving writer, and, calling me to his bedside, he told me there was something the matter with his lungs and he had to remain where he was another fortnight. I sat down beside him and began joking in the superior way healthy men adopt towards the sick. He never even asked me what I was doing there. The widow of an old friend then called to me and gave me a lengthy explanation about her kidneys. I reassured her, too. Afterwards, I glanced into a room containing two beds. The nurse told me that one of the patients had brain trouble. Would I come in, as he was awake and would be glad to see me? I said I would rather not disturb him and would come round next day.

In the morning I was unable to sleep. I tried to make some business calls on the phone, but could not get on to any one. At half-past nine I happened to stroll into one of the wards where an examination was being held. The Professor, a distinguished, quiet-voiced man whom I saw now for the first time, was standing beside a bed. A pretty girl student blushed as she answered his questions about the patient before her. 'And what else d'you see?' 'The abdominal muscles give under the hand, which shows that——' The girl hesitated and

89

looked intently at the patient. 'Well? Look at the eyes.' 'Icterus,' said the candidate with a sudden look of triumph. 'Bravo!' I whispered to myself, and in a moment the Professor was nodding his approval. Meanwhile, the patient looked with anxious eyes from one to the other.

At ten o'clock my first visitor arrived. He was brimming over with conventional high spirits. 'Well, old chap, so you've found a good way of doing nothing, eh? And I don't blame you, either. I've just brought you a little brandy and some good Egyptian cigarettes. What's that? You aren't smoking? What's the meaning of that? Lot of fuss to make over a little headache, isn't it? D'you know what *I* had to go through? Why, look, there's Imre! Hullo! Well, what d'you think of the old man?' By midday quite a little group had gathered, every one bringing a gift of some kind, flowers, eatables, or drinks. Bianka had prepared a veritable little banquet, consisting of a huge basketful of tropical fruit, tinned pineapples, and champagne. I sent back the hospital lunch uneaten. New visitors kept arriving, and at about half-past three, with a great hullabaloo, three of my journalist colleagues turned up from the newspaper offices, exuberant and noisy. 'What are you doing? What are we to write about you? What would you like us to say? Have you made any good jokes? You ought to, you know. It isn't a chance to miss.'

Their hilarity degenerated into boisterousness, with my guests egging one another on. As compared with

A Gesture in the Window-Pane

my feeling of anxiety of the previous day, I had nothing
to complain of. It was obvious that they were all fond of
me and did not resent my being here. Everything was
going to turn out all right. And yet . . . if that were so
. . . what was this strange anxiety coming over me . . . ?

You were so *very* cheerful, all of you. It was too much
of a good thing. Had you come to see me one by one, I
shouldn't have noticed anything. But this way it was
rather obvious that *every man jack of you* was bursting
with hilarity in exactly the same way. After all, there
are plenty of different temperaments in the world.
Didn't it occur to you that your uniform joviality in the
stalls made me all the more conscious of the stage on
which I stand alone here? A suspicion formed slowly in
my mind, to become a certainty at the last. You were
all *very silent* before you came into my room, and once
you left me again you were no less quiet. After a while
I could make out quite clearly how the new arrivals
hesitated a moment before entering the door and put a
mask on their faces. I almost saw them open their
mouths, force their expression into a smile, and make
their throats ready for laughter.

I turned thoughtfully towards the window, and for
a second I caught a glimpse of a little scene behind me
reflected in the glass. I saw Pista's head, as he stood at
the back of the room with his wife. He had a very long
face, the corners of his mouth were drawn down in a
gloomy expression, and he was frowning. I saw his wife

whisper something to him. Pista nodded, without turning his head. At the same time he made a gesture of resignation with his hand.

I burst out laughing, and every one looked at me in sudden amazement. 'It's nothing—nothing at all,' I assured them.' Just something that occurred to me. It's quite all right. Watch me—I'm going to have another drink!'

Hardly had my last visitor left the room, however, in the failing light, than I jumped up and began to dress, feverishly throwing on my clothes. First, I peeped into the corridor to see if it was empty. A doctor in his white coat was walking slowly up and down. I closed the door again. As soon as everything was quiet I put on my hat and coat, turned up the collar, and crept down the stairs like a thief. The porter did not see me as I turned into the deserted Ull Iöi-út. In the tram I bent my head down, so as not to be seen. On reaching my home I did not ring the bell, but slowly opened the hall door with my latch-key. Without being detected I crossed the bathroom to my own bedroom, closed the shutters, touched the familiar, flowered curtains, stretched myself on the divan, and shut my eyes. At nine o'clock Rózsi came, feeling her way in, and turned on the light. She started violently on catching sight of me. '*Jézus Mária, you* at home, sir?' 'It's all right, Rózsi. I don't want anything. I'm just going to sleep at home. Tell Cini to go to bed, too. If any one rings up, say I'll be phoning later. No, I don't want anything now—not even a book. I'm tired.

A Gesture in the Window-Pane

To-morrow morning, you say? We'll see about that when it comes. Good-night.'

I woke up at daybreak with so violent an attack of retching that I knew I could not play truant any longer. Rózsi came hurrying in and I tried to stammer out an excuse, showing her that I had been careful and had not been sick over anything. She gave me my clothes and I went straight back to the hospital, after telling her that I was to be found there if any one wanted me.

They were already waiting when I arrived. The doctor had been alarmed by my absence in the morning, and had been looking for me everywhere. I was to go at once to the laboratory for a blood and urine test. Those were the test bottles, please. . . . And the ceremony began all over again. First, I had my fingers pricked every half-hour with a hypodermic syringe. Then I went to the X-ray room, where my head was fastened between clamps and photographed from three sides. This over, I was taken back amongst the bottles, alembics, and measuring instruments. By midday it had been established that my sugar test was negative. Dr. Cs. was surprised that I took no interest in my X-ray reports, which were now ready. I shrugged my shoulders. I should know all in good time—what was the use of worrying? Oh yes, quite. . . . Then perhaps I would not mind stepping across to the ophthalmic section. A winding path led me through the gardens to the pavilion, where, after waiting a moment, I found myself once more in the dark room, confronted by the familiar ophthalmoscope, the field of vision disk, and the red and green spots. . .

I resigned myself to wait and asked no questions. A courteous ophthalmic surgeon informed me that in one eye the papilla showed a further deterioration of a diopter and a half.

I happened to be alone that afternoon, and, glancing through the books I had brought with me, I was surprised to see that they included the account of Scott's journey to the South Pole, which I had read before. And how vividly I remembered it! With this book in my hand I began a queer sort of reading. I could not see the print, but I knew exactly where I was as I turned the pages. Here, for instance, towards the end, was that simple and infinitely moving passage. The little band of five has set off with a dog sledge on the last lap of their trek. They reach the Pole, only to find Amundsen's flag floating where their fortunate rival had planted it two months previously, in a spot no man had ever reached before. Baffled and cheated of their aim, they set out on the return journey which none of them was to complete. The account of that terrible march was found a year later next to Scott's heart in the collapsed snow hut which was his tomb. Overtaken by a raging blizzard, with no possibility of escape, the members of the little band embraced one another and died. By now there were only three survivors, for Oates had walked out into the night and Evans had died on the way. Scott writes of Evans that he was no longer fully conscious in his last days. He trudged on mechanically through the blizzard, now stumbling blindly, now crawling on his knees or on all fours, not knowing where he was. From his delirious words the others knew that he was dreaming. A wonderful, ecstatic dream—for he spoke of walking through palm groves in the tropical twilight. This was one of the last notes Scott made, for, as he was soon to write: 'We shall stick it out to the end, but we are getting weaker, of course, and the end cannot be far. It seems a pity, but I do not think I can write any more.'

During the three days I had spent in hospital, I had only once laughed heartily and with real conviction. After a long evening walk I found a letter in my room. Erzsi D. had called to see me and, after waiting a long time, had written me the following lines: 'A sick man has the right to die, but not to go wandering about when his friends come to see him for the last time.'

One Tuesday morning at eleven o'clock the door opened and the Professor entered at the head of his white-uniformed staff, like the president of a court martial. He was holding my various reports in his hand. There were at least nine of them. I stood to attention like a soldier. In the midst of a respectful silence he proceeded to carry out a few rapid tests, then he made me stand by the window and looked intently at my face for a minute without speaking. There was an atmosphere of tense expectation. I felt sure that the moment had come when he would announce whether the investigation was to continue or whether I was to be handed over there and then for sentence to be pronounced. Or even . . . yes, it might even be . . . the verdict itself.

'Tell me, have you always had such thin eyebrows?'

The question took my breath away.

'Why . . . yes, Professor.'

The next moment he had turned away and, without another word, had marched out of the room at the head of his staff. (Weeks later I learnt that his question had been a perfectly legitimate, medical inquiry. I was sorry. It seemed to me more human and likeable as an absent-minded remark, for it would have shown that he was more interested by the man than by the patient.)

An hour later I was officially told that I could leave the hospital for the time being. No definite result having been obtained so far, I was to come back every five days. Imre called to fetch me away, and announced that a room had been taken for me at the Svábhegy Sanatorium.

9

In the Sanatorium

An air of quiet dignity pervaded the sanatorium on the hill. It was early spring, and there were hardly twenty people in the huge building. It was not yet known where I was, and for two whole days I lived in complete solitude. Each morning was a trial to me now, and I never went down into the hall. The feeling of nausea with which I awoke no longer vanished so promptly. In fact, a listlessness that resembled a state of coma remained with me now until lunch-time. Before dressing I would lie back in my arm-chair, rigid and shivering. In front of me, through the balcony window, I could see the marvellous phantasmagoria which was Budapest. What remained to me of consciousness struggled convulsively to maintain a hold on two focal points, my stomach and my brain. I concentrated on the former so that, as soon as it began to contract, I could drag myself to the wash-basin and mark time in front of it for half an hour with my head bent forward. I thought fixedly of my brain, so that I should have time to ring hastily for the attendant when

In the Sanatorium

I felt its powers failing. But I never rang, nor called for the doctor. At about three o'clock I would force myself to go down to the restaurant, where I would play with the dishes as if to suggest that they were a matter of real consequence to me. Afterwards, I pretended to doze off on a divan in some quiet corner. However, I could not sleep, as an old obsession was taking hold of me again. Somewhere behind the walls of my skull a cinema projector began to whir and I, a spectator in the dark hall, watched it go laboriously to work. The projector had a particularly hard task, as the pictures it had to throw on the screen were twenty years old. Moreover, they were faded and had not been properly exposed. The delicate film was all entangled and broken, so that the pictures would cease altogether for minutes at a time. My friend Gyula Havas's last days were the subject of this fitful shadow-play. At twenty-two years of age he had been both a passionate and gifted poet and a blind admirer of my own writings. This prejudice may have been mere self-admiration, for in our ways of thinking and imaginative outlook we resembled one another. I went to see him in hospital when he came back wounded from the front. He boasted to me how he had availed himself of the opportunity of being in the dressing-station to have a congenital fatty tumour removed from his chest. The surgeon had found some strange things inside it—a mass of hair and little bones. We laughed a lot about this, saying that maybe some new organ, hitherto unknown to man, was to have been born in him—some sixth sense

In the Sanatorium

or magnetic transmitter, and we jokingly anticipated broadcasting in days before it was invented. Then unexpected symptoms began to develop—headaches and paralysis. I remember it was then that I first heard of the fundus of the eye being tested. A tumour had formed on his brain. He himself gave me an account of its progress day by day, for, being young, he was not unduly anxious about it and curiosity was stronger in him than fear. Moreover, he never believed in death, at least not with his conscious mind. One morning he cheerfully recited to me his latest poem, which ended with these words in the mystico-melancholy vein then fashionable amongst the 'decadent' poets:

> *I gaze in the mirror,*
> *Stare long in the mirror,*
> *Then fling wide my arms. . . .*

'You see,' he explained, 'I'm saying good-bye to myself. Not bad, is it?' The poem was, in fact, a powerful one and it earned praise from that fine poet Árpád Tóth, a friend of ours who was the greatest master of the style. But Gyula Havas was to write no more. First, his neck became paralysed and twisted to one side—at least, that was the impression it made on me. Then the paralysis affected his legs, and he was obliged to lie sideways in the bed. By now he spoke hesitatingly and in a whisper, yet whenever I called to see him, he tried to joke and wink. This he could do only with one eye, for the other always remained open and looked as if it were bulging slightly out of his head. When I saw him for

In the Sanatorium

the last time alive he was lying quite motionless, with
his lower lip turned out as if he were laughing. And, in
fact, he was not at all depressed. He actually tried, with
a great deal of gasping and effort, to take off a friend of
ours who had been to see him half an hour before. This
friend had a nervous tic in the face, which poor Havas
did his best to imitate with strange grimaces. The next
time I saw him he was lying on the bier, and the expression on his face was ghastly.

The incessant strain of having to project these pictures again and again in my memory was becoming
unbearable. I would drag myself as far as the funicular
and sit down in the station. Perhaps Dénes would come
up on the next train and bring me some news, for I had
not seen a paper for three days. I felt I could not face
any more of these days made ominous and oppressive
by my Havas complex. I needed work to do, and I made
up my mind that I should spend the afternoon dictating
to Dénes. Thinking that I might perhaps be able to
read something in my notebook, I opened my eyes. It
was only a single word that I saw, but that word, written in four large letters, I read as unmistakably as if
some one had whispered: 'Móni.' Móni, Móni. . . . The
word had no meaning for me. There was something
written beside it, but this I could not read. And then
. . . a memory began to stir in me. My wife had spoken
of this Móni when she came home from the clinic
where she was working.

Móni, Móni, that was all I knew. Just the name

In the Sanatorium

Móni. I had never seen him, yet from a few words spoken at long intervals of time as he happened to crop up in conversation, I had a memory of him as coherent and vivid, as complete and firm in outline, as that I retained of my poor friend Havas. But, for all I knew, Móni was still alive.

Should I write a humorous fantasy about him? No, not that. He might lend himself better to a light character sketch. And I found myself already trying to construct his portrait from the meagre facts at my command.

MÓNI

One might see him any day amongst the harmless inmates of the asylum, going his round of the corridors. He would glance into the wards and in summer stroll out into the garden. He never interfered with any one, and it was rare for him to speak of himself. For twenty-five years he had lived in the institution, as a sufferer from schizophrenia. He had seen several generations of medical officers come and go, and two superintendents. But Móni never changed. To the attendants, the servants, and the patients as they came and went, he was the oldest acquaintance of all. The young doctors joked with him, and even the latest arrivals knew him as Móni. No one remembered his surname. It might have been Lefkovits or Perl—in any case, nobody cared. He was probably about sixty-

101

five, but this, too, was a matter of no significance. Every one knew that he had been a barrister, and some people still said 'sir' to him. As an inmate of the asylum there was little he had not seen in his time. He would turn up at the medical students' classes as if he were at home there, and would submit with a bored look when the lecturer gave a skilled account of his case to the students and visitors. 'Notice, gentlemen, this typical expression and gait. Just walk a few steps, Móni. You see the classical circumambulatory movement.' Móni would look about him as if the whole matter struck him as a bore. But when it came to question time, if a candidate hesitated, he would turn so that the Professor should not hear, and, a little ashamedly but with the best will in the world, he would hurriedly murmur the correct answer about his own illness with faultless medical terminology.

No one in the asylum ever remembered Móni having a visitor. He had lost his wife many years ago and his relatives, if he had any, had either died or forgotten about him. His mental affliction being absolutely harmless, they could have released him at any moment. But where were they to send him? He had neither home nor money. His old life, of which no one knew anything, had vanished leaving no trace, like the fabled Atlantis. The attendants had no time to accompany him, and if they had allowed him to go walking alone in the town he would have wandered away and forgotten to come back. Society would never have heard of him again. So they left him there to live out his days and his years in peace.

Perhaps, in the time before his illness, Móni had been an active, ambitious man. Strange as it appeared, he was still a highly educated man and had preserved his culture unimpaired. This was not apparent at the first glance. Móni spoke little and anything said in his presence was apt to leave him indifferent, as if he had not even heard it. But if some question of general knowledge were put to him, either on medical grounds or out of curiosity, Móni would give the correct answer, however difficult it might be. He never replied to such a question immediately, but would start mumbling to himself for a moment and afterwards give his answer. He had little contact with the other patients, either because they were of no interest to him or perhaps because he had grown too accustomed to them. Sometimes he would wander into a part of the asylum reserved for dangerous lunatics. This he did not because he had become one of them, but because he liked the change. His new surroundings never excited him, and he looked on with a calm and equable temper at the various manias and distorted visions of the world that greeted him there. My wife once spoke to me of a madman named Laci, a cunning, dangerous fellow who knew that he was mad and took advantage of the relative licence and exemption from the law which he enjoyed in consequence. He was a tall, thin young man with a black goatee beard—an odd mixture of Don

In the Sanatorium

Quixote and Lucifer. He had a trick of roaming about in a dressing-gown, his long arms crossed, picking his way stealthily like a horse and always remaining on tiptoe near the wall. He would walk about like this for hours on end, as if immersed in exciting thoughts. Nothing, however, escaped his notice. At such moments he was like some huge spider on the look-out for victims. And his victims were any one and every one whom he felt to be afraid of him. He would lie in wait for inexperienced young doctors working for the first time amongst dangerous lunatics, or women still under the influence of romantic ideas about insanity. If he came in contact with any one of this kind, a livelier expression would appear on his face, but he took care not to break out at once. Walking faster yet still more cautiously, he would pursue his rounds by the wall, observing them out of the corner of his eye. Suddenly, when they were least expecting it, he would rush up to his victim and make a lightning thrust at their eyes with two outstretched fingers. His object was apparently to frighten them and not to injure their eyes, for no sooner did he see his victims start back in alarm than he broke out into fiendish laughter, even if he had failed to touch his victim or if the attendants seized him in time. These outbursts of his so alarmed everybody that any other patient who happened to be near would make a rush for the door. Only Móni would remain calmly where he was, without even raising his eyes. He would merely shrug his shoulders and go on with his monotonous mumbling.

In the Sanatorium

Though Móni never interfered with any one or gave any trouble, he had his own deep-seated desires, to which he clung modestly and after his own gentle fashion. It was seemingly a question of habit with him, for he appeared not to notice that his desires were never realized. Had he forgotten about them, or did he know in his heart that they were unrealizable? Who could tell? One of his habits was to hang about, patiently and without obtruding himself on any one's notice, while the visiting physician went his rounds. As the doctor went out he would make his way up to him and hand him a sheet of paper. On the latter was written in his own handwriting: 'Patient No. 57 [himself] may leave the institution to-day.' This Móni handed to him with the gesture of one asking for an endorsement to render the document valid, so that he could walk out proudly once he had obtained it. When they returned it to him without a signature he never complained, but pocketed it and said nothing. Some of the doctors, who knew of this habit, would sign the paper or pretend to sign it, knowing very well that as a permit it was useless. The curious thing was that Móni behaved as if he, too, were quite aware of this. He would thrust the signed paper into his pocket as he did the others, and never made the slightest attempt to use it. In the depths of his mind there seemed to be a faint realization that it was only a joke after all.

There were, however, other indications which suggested that the longing for freedom had not died out in his withered soul. In the summer he liked to touch the

105

garden railing, and, holding two of the bars in his hands, he would stand for a long while gazing at the outer world. He, who took no interest in his fellow inmates, would scrutinize the passers-by minutely, wrinkling his forehead. In the winter he would stand for hours, bending over, beside the locked door. He never moved away on hearing the jingle of the key in the lock, and the person entering often knocked into him. He would stand with head bent, and did not realize when he was spoken to or when some one pushed him aside. Once he was seen to be examining the lock and handle. He did not press the handle down, but was fingering the lock.

Slowly, yet obstinately and perseveringly, as one who has forgotten what he wants yet knows that he wants something, he was passing his trembling old fingers, gently and without impatience, over the key-hole.

One day my wife happened to offer Móni a piece of chocolate, and she could see that the old man was very touched by this little attention. Though he never thanked her, she noticed on her next visit that he had carefully preserved the silver paper in which the chocolate had been wrapped. He had folded it up with infinite care and was holding it tightly clenched in his hand. Afterwards she often took him some little delicacy, for it struck her that he never had any visitors and never received anything of the kind. Móni always accepted the gift without speaking, and saved the paper to add to his collection. That she had begun to win his confidence was shown by the fact that henceforth he handed the permits only to her and left the other doctors alone. Sometimes he would follow her thoughtfully down the ward, as if he wanted to say something. But he never spoke, and the most good-humoured jokes and questions failed to draw an answer from him. It occurred to my wife that perhaps he was seeking for some kind of friendly contact with her, since she had succeeded in winning his confidence. One day she began to question him.

'How did you like that cake I gave you last time, Móni?'

True to his habit, Móni mumbled something to himself and eventually announced that the cake had been a good one.

Next, she ventured a surprise question, hoping as a doctor to ascertain whether the patient had his lucid moments.

'Tell me, Móni, who am I?'

Móni looked up at her for a second and then, perhaps for the first time, gave her an answer without the usual lengthy gibberish.

'Malvin Brüll.'

My wife was puzzled by the unknown name. On her afternoon visit to the ward it came back to her mind, and she asked him another question.

'Móni, who's Malvin Brüll?'

And, raising his head, Móni gave her the simple answer:

'My mother.'

107

10

The Gyulas hold a Council[1]

Somewhere in the darkness of my skull, as I sat in the more spacious twilight of the sanatorium, Fate was slowly and inexorably at work. Far beyond either, that mysterious something, the Unknown, had also begun to stir; that something which we know only indirectly and for a brief while, and of which every man is the only centre and the only certainty. In a mysterious way the Outer World began to send its vibrations through the darkness.

Behind the walls of my skull something was happening. What it was I knew less than any one. Even the others could do no more than guess. Those walls inclosed a soft, rubber-like mass the convolutions and yellowish-white colour of which are so strikingly similar to the kernel of a walnut as almost to convey a warning. At one particular point in this mass a process of some kind was beginning. For the moment it was im-

---

[1] In very early times, the 'gyulas' were counsellors who advised the Magyar chieftain on matters of war and policy. The word is now of frequent occurrence as a Christian name.

possible to say where it had started. Perhaps it was located in the centre between what one might call the two upper quarters of the walnut kernel, or down in the prolongation of the brain where the tiny gland lies that governs growth and sexual character. Maybe it was in the outer membrane behind the forehead, or again deep in the grey matter itself. It might be high up at the back of the skull, or low down in the region of the cerebellum. And the nature of the trouble was still equally mysterious. Perhaps it was no more than a slight hardening, comparable to a flaw in a grain of wheat; after causing me no trouble ever since my birth, it might suddenly have begun to grow, now that I was past the meridian of life. Maybe the membrane had started to swell out into a cyst, and the latter, as it filled with fluid, was continually dilating and forcing back the substance of the brain in its effort to make room for itself. Or a vein might have become choked and swollen with the blood no longer able to pass freely through it. Or again, two small veins, which had hitherto flowed in parallel courses, might possibly have run together and united their blood streams.

From the point of view of the trouble itself, the question of where it started and at what precise spot it had taken root was one of complete indifference. But not so to me. As far as the disease was concerned, it could be no more than a question of material to go to work upon. The essential problem for it was whether it would prove stronger or weaker in the tussle with its surroundings. From my point of view, the question resolved itself into an exciting game of hazard. I had to try and guess at which precise spot in that bony roulette table the ball had come to rest. For those various sections of my brain, if taken together, composed a something known to me as 'I'—one thinking and talking, another counting, a third imagining, a fourth longing and suffering, a fifth remembering and dreaming, while a sixth wrought ecstasy of heart and the banishment of pain.

I was familiar with them all. Yet not one of them had a direct perception, either as pain or pleasure, of what was going on in the Unknown. Nor did my sense of the improbable and the fantastic grasp the fact that something which concerned both of these was afoot. It did not realize that one tiny link in the chain of human life had developed a flaw and was about to give way. Nor did it observe that this had started throughout the huge chain of which the link formed part a minute, almost imperceptible trembling, as when a tiny electric spark sets all the firmament vibrating round it. Without knowing that it did so or wishing to do so, the chain was about to resist this break in its continuity. Life, which is ever seeking after form and which extinguishes life that itself may live, was now gathering its forces *as a whole* to resist this formless interference from without. It seemed that life still had a use for the tiny cell which was 'I', and would not abandon me without a struggle. Instead of allowing me to be devoured, the species was now to stand up in defence of the one who had so often stood up for it.

110

The Gyulas hold a Council

But this purpose became a conscious one only in the case of a few.

It was early morning. A workman had set out, with a good deal of grumbling, to walk from his home in the Zugliget towards the centre of the city. His little boy had woken up with a sore throat; he was feverish and had cried a lot. His wife had been on at him about it. He was to be sure and call at the children's hospital to ask them when she could bring the child next day.

It annoyed him to have to go out of his way. A good drink would have been more to his liking, but when a man had a wife and children. . . . What did she want, anyway? Wasn't she satisfied now that he'd married her, without going and landing him with this . . . ? He was still feeling disgruntled as he sat down on a wooden bench in the out-patients' room. Next to him a little boy sat crying, with his head in a bandage. The sound went to his heart and, by the time he stood up in front of the grave-looking, bearded doctor, he was glancing about him with a timid, anxious expression. 'Well, young man, what can I do for you?' 'If you please, sir, it's my little boy.' 'Little boy? Very well. Where is he?' 'I haven't brought him, sir—his mother'll be bringing him to-morrow, er—I mean if . . .' 'Look here, what d'you take me for? A doctor or a telescope? You run home and bring me the child. . . . Just wait a moment, though. Where do you live? Ah, ha! Let's see. . . . I'll come round myself this afternoon. Good morning! Next, please!'

111

The Gyulas hold a Council

As he hurried in the direction of the wards after his consulting hour, the doctor was smiling. They were too absurd, these poor people! There was that workman, for instance. And what was it the other fellow said about being 'axe-rayed'? He had meant to write it down for Frici Karinthy . . . Karinthy! That was a piece of luck—just the man he was after! He would go and see him that afternoon at six. The tram for the Zugliget stopped just opposite the Café Central, where he was always to be found. Yet, now that he came to think of it, didn't Gyula mention something about him the other day . . . ? Yes, that was it. Wasn't he expecting some reports on him soon? He'd ring up now and make sure. 'That you, Gyula? Géza speaking. I was just wondering about Frici Karinthy. Yes. . . . Yes. . . . Yes. What d'you say? Ah, ha! As serious as that, is it? What's that? You were just going to ring me up? Who else? A consultation on him . . . ? Where? Right you are. . . . Let's say half-past four. I just wanted to see him. You say he's on the Svábhegy? Good thing you told me. Well, I'll be there at half-past four. Whoever'ud have thought that was going to happen to *him*? He's never been ill in his life. Well, thanks for telling me. Good-bye.'

On the Andrássy-út, a man stood at the entrance to his shop complaining bitterly to his brother-in-law. 'I can't make a do of it, anyhow. I tell you, it's a hell of a world. Take that wool tie over there. It was all the rage —now there's no getting rid of it. That writer fellow

told me he'd buy half a dozen . . . I haven't seen him
for two months. They say he's got his head swollen or
something. I don't wonder, in times like these.'

The bus was leaving for Vienna at half-past one. A
married couple had just started to say good-bye. 'Hurry
up, or you'll go and miss it! What are you staring at?
That English aeroplane? Flying pretty low, isn't it? I
call it tempting Providence—look, he's only just cleared
the roof! Well, you won't forget to ring up Aranka at
the clinic? About Frici, you know. . . . Tell her it
might be better if she . . . No, after all, don't tell her
anything. I don't think she knows. You might ask her
to ring me up, when you get a chance. . . . Well, good-
bye, Olga! So long, Jenö! Behave yourself!'

Work began at six o'clock that morning in the Krupp
armaments factory, where they were turning out a
new type of machine-gun for aeroplanes.

At a factory in Helsingfors, a perspiring mechanic
was at work on a new instrument of another kind. A
famous surgeon had asked him to carry out some seemingly insignificant improvements, which were nevertheless improvements. For some years past he had operated exclusively on the brain, a branch of surgery which
had come very much to the fore as a result of brilliant
results achieved by an American pioneer. It had occurred to him that if the blade of the instrument could
be fitted on a swivel so that it could turn freely and be
introduced under the cerebellum, without having to be

113   H

continually taken out and applied again, this would be a most important step. He had an idea for an entirely new kind of operation, never yet performed. The edge of the blade would have to be sharpened as well as the tip, and it should be narrow enough for the surgeon to use it between the haemostatic forceps. The mechanic was concentrating on his work, the grinder emitted a regular scream as it sharpened the blade and the blade screamed as it grew sharper under the stone.

'Have you heard what's wrong with Frici Karinthy?'

'Yes, I did hear something, but it isn't . . . ?"

'What d'you mean, it isn't . . . ? He's as good as done for.'

'Then don't let's talk about it! It's dreadful, the things you hear. . . .' But, as he walked on, his step became lighter and more elastic. He whistled a snatch or two and wagged his head. 'So that'll be another one gone!' he reflected absent-mindedly, still whistling. 'Well, thank Heavens, now they can give D. a chance to take his place on the paper. I'll tell V. to send poor Karinthy something. I suppose he's past working now.'

The great lyrical poet came sauntering down a little street in Buda. He was alone and wrapped in thought. Something he had just read about me was on his mind. The news had deeply affected him and brought back a train of memories. He thought of all the times we had spent together and the tears came to his eyes, as he felt that we were together once more in the spirit. Yes, it had been very beautiful. And now the opportunity had come. . . . He really ought to write about it all. What a piece of luck! Providence had created me so that that obituary notice might be written. He would let the review have it immediately after my death. Poor fellow. . . . Yes, he would begin with that story of mine about the clown who balances the chairs on one another and, when he reaches the top, takes out the violin he longed to play as a boy. Just at that moment he would make the whole edifice collapse. Perfect! Couldn't be better! A living symbol! It would be my whole life in an obituary notice. The great poet was quite genuinely moved.

And so the wave spread outwards in space, but perhaps not only in space. Did not its ripples extend backwards through time as well?

For example, those four serious heads in a quiet corner of one of the cafés beside the Danube? Were they not phantoms from the distant past? Surely they were the *gyulas* sitting in council, those advisers of the ancient Magyars who met before a decisive battle to discuss the counsel they were to give the chieftain, so that he should emerge from the encounter in triumph or at least with a whole skin. They, too, dealt in auguries and omens and paid particular attention to those animal intestines from which the future could be read.

Two of them actually bore the name of Gyula— Absent-Minded Gyula and Matter-of-Fact Gyula—

both excellent friends of mine. One of them is always in the clouds, listening and talking but continually turning his head away, so that one never knows what is in his mind. The other sat next to him in a rigid attitude. With his head bent down and narrow mouth tightly drawn, he seemed to be taking stock of the invisible problem before him like a bull about to charge. One felt that he was always strictly at his post, and that he would take care not to devote to the solution of any given problem one iota more or less of energy than it demanded. Géza was there, too, in a grey suit as usual. He had just come from examining the workman's child, and next day he was to complete his study of the conditions governing bone-formation in childhood. The most taciturn of the four, he sat listening and blinking with a thoughtful expression. Though very sleepy, he did not doze off. He spoke seldom, and when he did so it was in a quiet, restrained tone. He would often clip his vowels, as if anxious to save time for more important matters. The fourth member of the group, Endre M., a brilliant surgeon, was a tall, smartly dressed man with an ironical expression that suggested at once the intellectual and the man of the world. His career, which had begun in a steeply mounting curve, had now settled down on the broad, uniform path of success, as he abandoned the dreams of youth for the serious work of manhood. His travels had taken him about the world, and he had been invited to the consultation as a pupil of the Boston doctor who was one of the pioneers of modern brain surgery.

The Gyulas hold a Council

The discussion had already begun. Absent-Minded Gyula was meditatively turning his head away. Matter-of-Fact Gyula was examining the reports which he had meticulously collected and numbered the day before. On the table before him lay the X-ray of my brain, the ophthalmic report, and those from the hospital. No definite diagnosis had as yet emerged, but all the reports unfortunately pointed to a single conclusion.

The discussion turned on my brain, my whole brain and nothing but my brain. Nobody uttered a word about me. Each of those four men was as warmly attached *to me personally* as I to him. One of them was united to me by an almost brotherly affection, which was far stronger than mere gratitude or esteem and a kind of answer to my own unanalysable affection for him. There was not one of the four whose pity I should not value more than the admiration of some simple soul. Yet, if I had seen them there, perhaps I should have misunderstood their attitude. I should have expected something *more* than the masculine reserve with which they veiled their emotional reactions. A stranger might have imagined that they had never set eyes on the man whose fate they had met to discuss, on their own initiative and without his knowledge. Absent-Minded Gyula spoke only on points of detail, with an occasional sigh and with numerous reservations, as if he felt inclined to withdraw all he had said at the first sign of opposition. His 'humble opinion' floated above the table as languidly as an evening

breeze passing over the autumnal cornfields. Matter-
of-Fact Gyula stated his views with a polite, almost
blood-curdling, decisiveness. Géza frequently nodded
his head, and only managed to keep awake with an
effort. The surgeon quoted an abundance of modern
instances from his own experience. He had already
made up his mind what he would recommend when
the others announced their diagnosis, the nature of
which he never doubted for a moment.

'Well, gentlemen, unless I am mistaken, we have
decided to complete these excellent hospital reports
with the help of a special neurological diagnosis. If we
regard the latter as final, we shall then be in a position
to decide whether anything is to be done. My own feeling, I regret to say, is that something will have to be
done, and done quickly. That rapid deterioration of the
papilla isn't a good sign. I should suggest. . . .'

'There's the question of expense,' sighed Absent-
Minded Gyula. 'Will he have enough money?'

'That's another matter,' interposed Matter-of-Fact
Gyula curtly. 'It'll be time to talk about that when we
know what we're going to do.'

'Then there's the neurological examination. Shall
we send him to R. again?'

No, that was no good. Frici didn't like him. He was
obstinate about it, though nobody knew why.

'Yes, of course. Patients get those ideas. In any case,
a clinical examination would be better. What about
the——?'

The Gyulas hold a Council

'I believe his wife's in Vienna, at the Wagner-Jauregg clinic. Wouldn't it be better for him to go there?'

'Very good idea. They've got all the equipment and P.'s a first-rate diagnostician. I'll go up to the sanatorium this afternoon and tell him tactfully that'll be the best thing—don't you think?'

The question, uttered in an indecisive tone, had been addressed to Matter-of-Fact Gyula, whose thick brows showed darkly above eyes that were fixed on some invisible object. They looked like a line drawn under the most important words of a sentence, and admitting of no contradiction. He did not answer, which meant that he was on the track of another solution.

'It'll be better if I go,' he remarked after a moment's thought. 'He's got to be told clearly. We can't go beating about the bush.'

And, sure enough, he appeared that afternoon in the dimly lighted hall where only three of us were sitting. I was just enjoying a little discussion that was going on between two popular actresses. One of these was a comédienne and the other had made a name by her performances in strong parts. They were both equally young, but the comédienne addressed the other with the awed respect of a débutante talking to a great tragic actress. Her colleague was choking with indignation.

'Hullo, Gyula! Glad to see you, old chap. Come and sit down.'

He listened patiently, with his head bent down, while I chattered to him of one thing and another. Then, all of a sudden, he turned to face me.

119

The Gyulas hold a Council

'Look here—I'm motoring down to the country to-morrow morning for a ten days' rest. Care to come with me?'

I smiled.

'Think it would do me good? Is that why you came?'

For the first time in my life, I seemed to have detected an inconsistency in him. The question appeared to embarrass him a trifle.

'It would be the best thing possible for you, man. Let everything go to Hell. What you want's a rest. You mustn't think, you mustn't see anybody, you mustn't work, you mustn't even talk. . . .'

That evening, however, there came the long ring on the telephone which meant an inter-urban call. It was Vienna speaking. My wife's words came tumbling helter-skelter out of the phone.

'Heavens alive, man, what's the matter with you? I've just been speaking to Jenö. D'you mean to say you've had a choked disk without letting me know a word about it? Well, I'm leaving in an hour's time, d'you hear. . . ? I shall be in Budapest first thing in the morning. . . . What a thing to go and do . . . ! I don't know how you could. . . . To think you've known all about it for a fortnight . . . and it never even occurred to you . . . that here was I——'

'Three minutes, please!'

As day broke, my wife came hurrying in.

11

Return to the Scene of the Crime

Vienna again.

We arrived in the evening by the Árpád rail car. I had an attack of giddiness and complained bitterly that this new means of locomotion was no good, as it swayed both horizontally and vertically. I refused to believe that others did not have the same feeling, and that I experienced it only because my sense of balance was upset. We stayed at the Hôtel de France. The whole town had an air of dejection about it, especially in that district. Every one looked disgruntled and suspicious. I swore audibly in the ill-lighted streets, as we went up the stairs, and again when we reached our room. Eventually I realized that no one was answering me back. The others looked uncomfortable, but said nothing. So I left off all of a sudden.

At ten o'clock next morning I called at the Wagner-Jauregg clinic.

Not until I found myself unwillingly plodding up the steps at last, after all my procrastinations and prevarications and all my excuses and pretexts for postponing the evil day, did I realize with a profound sense of discouragement what it was that I found so repellent there. On that very staircase I had stood three weeks ago—only three weeks, yet they seemed as long as my whole lifetime! It was on that spot that I had flung out, as frivolously as if they had been some grotesque or flippant joke, the words, 'I've got a tumour on the brain. . . .'

I knew that the idea in my mind was an insane delusion and my education and scientific instinct rose up to protest against it, but superstitions of this kind have haunted me all my life. As I stood there I could not rid myself of the notion that my trouble began only when I spoke about it. Not only was it born at that moment, but *as a direct result* of my having given it a name. I felt that things happened because we gave names to them, and thus came to look upon them as possibilities. Everything we regard as possible comes to pass. Reality is the child of man's imagination. In my own case, I had led the investigators to follow a single trail, thus *diverting* their attention from others and perhaps from the true one. I feel obliged to record this obsession, as otherwise the reader would not understand my frame of mind, and I, too, would find it incomprehensible. The anxious, eerie sensation that weighed on me as I passed down those echoing corridors was exactly like that experienced by a criminal revisiting the scene of his crime.

I found myself wondering nervously whether the doctor, the secretary, and the nurse whom I had seen

122

on the first occasion would still be there. It was only when I myself felt a touch of hysteria in this self-questioning that I realized what I had been unconsciously looking for. It was that unknown patient in the neurological section whose face had been somehow familiar to me. I asked what had become of him, but no one seemed to remember. Was I sure he had been in that ward? Could I say which bed he was in? The third? Oh, of course, that was poor Diegel! He went a fortnight ago. 'Exit,' as the nurse said.

The Professor was not expected till later in the morning. Meanwhile, a sad-faced house physician plied me with questions in a gentle voice, and the opticians swung my head about like a rickety old camera. There was a continual noise going on in the room where this took place, the unfamiliar faces got on my nerves and the constant flow of German became an agony to my ear. At length, a modest young doctor recognized me, and this made me feel more at home. He had been in the clinic for two years, working on a discovery of his regarding the cure of schizophrenia by insulin.

After a long while Professor Pötzl arrived. Everything about him—the striking head, the expression, the eyes, the gestures—spoke of the true-born artist. Intelligence, skill, fervour, and self-control were written in all his features—traits which the poet shares with the acrobat. His almost exaggerated courtesy was not unattractive, betraying as it did a streak of absent-mindedness, which commands both sympathy and respect on the part of those who understand. He apologized for bringing me out, as he would have come round to my hotel if he had had time. Incidentally, he had heard all about me. Perhaps I knew that his father had been one of Vienna's most famous humorists. He never even alluded to medical matters, yet after a moment or two I began to feel as confident as a passenger on a ship in peril when he hears that the captain has personally taken over the helm. He wanted me to remain in the clinic until the examination was over, but he at once agreed to let me spend every second night in the hotel.

During the next week this semblance of freedom kept my spirits up. Without it I should have felt myself as good as sentenced, for this examination was no longer the easy-going, playful, deceptive game it had been at home. There every one knew and took an affectionate interest in me, as I in them. To the people here I was a *case* and nothing more—a mass of data in a leather bag. I was like a newly recruited soldier who has to be put in a uniform and drilled before being drafted to his proper unit. Or perhaps more like a criminal upon whom sentence has not yet been passed but who is certain to be declared guilty, and has thus to all intents and purposes begun to serve his time.

Even the prison itself, as seen by my impressionistic eyes, bore a resemblance to those older establishments of the Inquisition. It amused me to compare these rooms full of medical apparatus to torture chambers, and, extending the analogy step by step, I noticed that even the window in my room was set as high as in those old cellars. I ragged the kindly nurses, calling them hirelings of the rack-master. By now I went through the eye, ear, and nerve tests like an old hand, and joked about them as if they were nothing to me. But one day I left off joking and opened my eyes. They were beginning to carry out tests that were new to me, things I had never seen before. They tested my sense of smell, to see whether I could distinguish between garlic and wild strawberries, and my palate, to find out if I were confusing tastes. Then they put me strange questions. I had to reply instantly, to add up and subtract. After a handwriting test they asked me suddenly if I knew who Napoleon was. What was the idea? An intelligence test or an elementary general knowledge paper? Had I come to that? It seemed so.

From that moment I began to watch myself intently. I was constantly on my guard, weighing every word and gesture. Next day, when they subjected me to a further reflex test, I behaved like a man accused of something. The numerous examinations I had undergone in Budapest were of assistance to me here. While I knew in advance what was coming, I acted as if I had no idea what it was all about. Then, with a tremendous effort, I produced the reflexes of a healthy man. But they were not to be taken in by my performance. They said nothing and just went on with the tests. I learnt afterwards from the diagnosis that I 'came a cropper', as the slang phrase has it, over a silly 'cross-question' which proved decisive evidence against me. I had forgotten to be on my guard for dysmetria! In itself, this symptom looks trivial enough. If the patient opens his arms horizontally while keeping his eyes closed, he lifts one a shade higher than the other. There's nothing in that, one feels inclined to say. Yet this is an infallible proof that a breakdown has occurred on that particular side of the brain, and usually in the cerebellum. The *cold water test* which goes with this (and which was invented by the Hungarian Nobel prizewinner Bárány) escaped my notice altogether when the water was poured into my ear.

I now observed a curious new symptom in myself. I began to have frequent dreams, and the interesting point was that I remembered them so clearly that they were sometimes more vivid than the events of the day. These dream pictures were sharply imprinted on my mind, for there was nothing wrong with my eyes in sleep. I have a most vivid memory of one particular dream. The distribution of light and shade was clearer in the following scenes than in the experiences of my waking hours. I dreamt I was leading a political party and making a big speech in Parliament. My arguments were clear, logical, and convincing, and I emphasized them with easy, graceful gestures. I outlined a scheme of reforms the nature of which I remember quite distinctly. When the division came, it seemed likely that I should become Prime Minister. At that moment a great lout with bloodshot eyes jumped up, not from the Opposition benches, but through a trap-door under the table in the centre. He began shouting in a hoarse voice

Return to the Scene of the Crime

—some sort of gibberish which I did not understand. His mouth looked like a black whirlpool as it snapped at the air. I caught the words, 'Treating symptoms—treating symptoms—we've had enough of treating symptoms. Down with the moneyed classes! Down with 'em! Down with 'em!' I tried to silence him, then to win him over by argument, but he only made an angry gesture as if to brush away some contemptible, whimpering interruption. The next moment I realized that I had only succeeded in making a little whimpering noise. . . . My father was making signs to me from a dark doorway and pointing excitedly to his mouth for me to stop the man shouting. At least, I ought to tell him not to tap-dance and make a din, or Gasparecz, who lived in the flat underneath ours, would wake and come up. I felt the blood stop in my veins with fright, for Gasparecz was a name frequently mentioned in my childhood. But now the speaker was tap-dancing faster and faster. He was no longer talking, but only giggling and dancing, while from my throat, instead of an energetic call to order, there came an ever feebler and shriller sound of whimpering, until the moment I woke up.

The tedious noise kept pace with me as I shuffled down the Alserstrasse, pestering me even when awake. For the whole thing was becoming a whine and a bore. Somewhere behind me an unseen beggar with a hurdy-gurdy was grinding out a tune which I heard only as I walked. As soon as I stopped and swung round, it vanished. I was weary, unutterably weary of it all, weary of sickness and weary of death, which I did not find terrifying or moving or impressive or overwhelming, but just a nuisance, like some slinking, treacherous dog for ever tracking me down.

It got on my nerves, too, that I kept walking with my feet turned in and that, as my sight was bad, I could not see to correct my step and was constantly going into the gutter or knocking against the wall. And that I kept lurking shamefacedly in a corner or hiding for hours in a cold lavatory. And that the chauffeur stood watching me sympathetically as I got out of the car, gasping for breath. Buddha and Confucius I found wearisome, too. They got on my nerves whether I looked them in the face or turned my back on them. Give me Democritus or that other pagan philosopher who lifted his unseeing eyes disdainfully towards the sun which blinds those who have sight!

One morning I woke up in a hilarious frame of mind. My old friend the kindly, sad-eyed Jóska, used to look in faithfully every morning and entertain me with his gurgling laugh. On this occasion I at once began to tell him my dream. 'Listen to this one, Jóska! I was going up to the clinic as usual with my wife. It was ten o'clock but, funnily enough, Pötzl had got there before us. He was all smiles, though you could see he was annoyed because we were late. My wife began to excuse herself. "Ach, garnichts, garnichts, Gnädige! I assure you, it's really nothing." All the same, I felt that something was wrong, but I kept smiling politely so as not to let him see. I enumerated my symptoms in a chatty, humorous tone and laid the reports before him with explanations like a bookseller exhibiting his catalogues. "Hier Röntgenbefund, nicht wahr, Herr Professor, hier Staungspapillae, nicht wahr, auch erwähnungswert. . . ." He listened to me very politely, screwing up his eyes as I babbled on. I still felt that something was wrong and I soon saw his face darken. It was an insignificant little report that came next, and the fat was in the fire. "Hier Patellen-Reflex. . . ." I tried to improve the occasion. "Apart, sehr hübsch, wirklich . . . ich würde sehr empfehlen. . . ." But he had jumped to his feet and his alarmingly tall figure was looming over me. He flung out his arms, and I saw the long fingers tremble as he clutched at me. "Wa . . . a . . . as? Pat-tel-len?" he yelled. "Marsch hinaus!" My wife tried to pacify him— "Aber, Herr Professor . . . ! As a doctor, I——" but he no longer saw or heard anything. He flung himself on us and we shrank back in terror, till we could turn and rush down the stairs. He came after us like a madman, a gigantic figure of a man, cursing in Hungarian. Stumbling and scrambling, we managed to get down the stairs and out into the street. We could see only one foot now, as his huge figure came crashing after us, but his voice was still booming out, "How dare you, sir? Talk to me about patella reflexes!"'

That morning I was still in buoyant spirits at the clinic as a result of my dream. I almost dreaded meeting the Professor for fear I should laugh in his face. As for the sad-faced house physician with the gentle voice, I could not leave him alone. I ragged and teased him till even he laughed. Soon, however, I saw him blush, and, raising his voice in an unaccustomed way, he remarked almost angrily: 'Ich muss Sie daranf aufmerksam machen, dass Sie schwer krank sind—Sie dürfen nicht so lustig sein.' I quieted down a little after that, but asked leave to go out to luncheon.

In the taxi I felt thoroughly offended. 'Schwer krank' —what rubbish! They hadn't even diagnosed my illness. What business was it of his, anyhow? When the diagnosis was announced I should behave accordingly, but for the time being I was ill, and that was all there was to it. If I happened to be on the sick list, I was in all other respects the same as any man who had a perfect right to behave as he wished. I threw my head back self-consciously. An attack of nausea was just coming on, but what of that?

Yes, I felt sick again all of a sudden. I was ill, and that was that. Besides, what if I were ill? Hadn't I the right to be? Just like any one else? And to die, if I wanted to? If that was all life had to offer . . . it wouldn't matter much to me. . . . And if I didn't amount to more than the arrogant, supercilious, healthy fellows I saw round me my loss wouldn't count for much, either. . . . Perhaps they thought I valued this poor sickly life of mine more than the healthy ones they flaunted in front of me.

'Driver! Bleiben Sie stehen!'

130

Return to the Scene of the Crime

I stepped out of the taxi and stood a moment on the kerb. All of a sudden I began to retch in the midst of the busy street—arrogantly, insolently, without shame. The passers-by stopped to look at me, some indignantly shaking their heads, others merely gaping. One youth gave a coarse laugh. Go on, gentlemen, go on, stare at me—gaffen Sie nur, Herrschaften! I'm retching. Would you believe it? And anyway, what's it matter to you? I'm ill—I'm on the sick list. I've got the right to do this sort of thing, you haven't. Now you can see for yourselves—I'm throwing up. Just step in, ladies and gentlemen—this way! Here you can come and see by my vomiting what I think of you and of me and of my whole life and what I've been able to make of it! Here you can see it on the pavement of a Viennese street! You can see my life spewing back with thanks the wondrous gifts of which the giver was so proud, and which have brought him who received them to the pretty pass you see!

Nevertheless, by eight o'clock that evening I was sitting on the terrace of the Café de France in the cold April wind. I was not joking or cursing now, or even talking at all. My head ached. I was thinking of the pain, and wondering how it was possible for physical agony to be so intense. I had never imagined that such torture could be endured. Yet here was I, both conscious and able to think clearly. And not only to think, but to observe the process and make calculations about it. The steel circle round my skull was closing in with

131

faint cracking noises. How much farther could it shrink? I counted the cracking sounds. Since I took the triple dose of pain-killer, there had been two more. . . . I took out my watch and laid it on the table.

'Give me some morphia,' I said in a calm, hostile, icy tone.

'You mustn't take morphia! You know perfectly well. The very idea! And what are you doing with that watch?'

'You will give me morphia within three minutes.'

They looked me uneasily up and down. No one moved. Three minutes went by. Then ten more. I slipped the watch calmly into my pocket and rose unsteadily to my feet.

'Then take me to the Fiakker Bar. They say it's a good show, and to-night I want to enjoy myself.'

The others jumped up with a feeling of relief.

I never confessed the secret to any one, either then or afterwards. I had made up my mind at the end of those three minutes—for the first and last time in my life—that if my headache had not stopped within the next ten I should throw myself under the nearest tram.

It never came out whether I should have kept to my resolve, for the pain left off with the suddenness of lightning.

12

Visitors

A big surprise was in store for me. One anxious day a week later I called on the Professor to hear the verdict, and was told that no decision had been arrived at. Placing the tips of his fingers together, as if in prayer, and smiling benignly, the artistic-looking Pötzl made me a guarded announcement based on the tests so far completed. In his view, a cyst full of fluid was growing on the right side of my cerebellum. He also had other suspicions, but for the present he would say nothing about this. Before coming to a final decision he wished to make an experiment. If the fluid could be absorbed internally, the cyst would go down and the pressure would be relieved. He therefore wished to try the effect of a mercury ointment which absorbed fluid. This I was to apply for a week while living on a special diet, and it might perhaps prove successful. When the week was up I was to come and see him again.

A week seemed a long time, and I was desperately anxious to spend it in Budapest. With a tremendous effort, I accomplished the journey, and, once home again, took to my bed, which I had no desire to leave. Every other day I coated a different part of my body with the grey ointment at half-hour intervals.

I found the sensation of having no work to do strange but enjoyable. I had no plans, no responsibilities. The ointment seemed to be doing me good; some of my symptoms disappeared and for a whole day I had no nausea. I just let things take their own way, lying phlegmatically in bed and watching other people.

For I was not alone. An army of visitors came thronging into my flat in the big house where I was then living in the Reviczky-ucca. To my delight, more and more of them kept coming. The crowds of people were an occupation and an entertainment to me. My feeling of exhaustion when they left me late at night was easy to bear. The telephone rang constantly, but, if it was quiet for half an hour, I would take up the receiver myself to invite some one.

I found pleasure in studying their characters with the eye of a connoisseur. I saw the position clearly. *Sympathy*, which is the most sensational faculty of man, was holding an exhibition of its positive and negative manifestations. Orgies of sympathy were going on around my room, in the arm-chairs, on the divan and on the edge of my sick-bed. Two extremes were noticeable amongst these sympathetic friends. There was the noisy, exuberant, jocular type, who affected to treat the whole matter as a mere bagatelle, and, by making light of it, sought to hide the panic which steals over every one in presence of the great Enigma that awaits us all. Then there were the quiet, serious ones, braver than the first, who had examined their own hearts and knew that there can be no sympathy without egoism. It is the elder sister of sympathy, our own fear of death, which introduces us to it when the first danger threatens us in childhood. From that day we can sympathize with others.

There was also a third type—utterly frank, straightforward, and without false scruples. I received a letter from a relative of mine who said he had heard that I was about to 'leave them'. In view of his serious situation, he hoped I would not forget him. I was to be sure and arrange for him to receive 300 pengoes on the day I 'went away'. This, to say the least of it, was plain speaking, which required no psychological analysis to be understood.

During all this time four or five people would be sitting in my room at once, while others were having refreshments in the dining-room or playing bridge. I took a delight in all this continual movement, and to this day I am grateful to those who were responsible for it. To Bébi, for instance, who so wisely understood that I needed a lighter and yet more stimulating spiritual food, which she provided not only by giving me the pleasure of her own company but also by bringing with her people whom I had never met before. These meetings had a special charm, as they made me feel in the swing of things. I am grateful to Rózsi K., who spoilt me with *eau de Cologne*, fruit, and a dressing-gown, to

Visitors

Laci, who brought me the literary gossip of the town, to Oszkár, who supplied me with good stories and imitated my fellow writers, to Bandi, who gave me an animated account of the novel on which he was working, and to Andor, with whom I regaled myself over old memories like a gourmet enjoying the flavour of a 'ripe' cheese. I made it a point of honour not to let them be bored, and bored they were not. The pains I took to achieve this end were repaid when I saw how even old enemies became reconciled in the general atmosphere of good humour around my sick-bed. I prevailed upon as many of the guests as possible to remain to dinner, and our conversations dragged on into the small hours.

Meanwhile the outer world, reacting unconsciously to my illness, pursued its unobtrusive, life-saving errand.

Sometimes it seemed that all was not going smoothly. It was as if an extraordinary session of Parliament were being held to discuss the problem of my life or death. They were now sitting continuously—though, of course, none of them knew himself to be a member of that Parliament—and their debate was on the line of policy to be adopted. The discussion centred on two points: what was to be done, and, when this had been decided, how should they set about persuading me tactfully to accept their decision?

The Gyulas came to see me twice, but they were not together and they never spoke to me of the future.

Visitors

Though we argued and joked a lot, I had not the least idea what they really thought about me. One morning I got up and asked to be taken to the newspaper office. When I arrived every one was full of kindness and tact, and they all took care not to let their sympathy become obvious. Nobody stood round gazing at me as if a miracle had happened, but every one went on with his work as usual. Only the secretary, Mr. Láng, hesitated for a moment when he saw that I could not find the handle of the editor's door. One of the directors pretended he had suddenly remembered a little detail when he caught sight of me. ('Now you're here, you might just come up to my office for a moment!') He closed the door and thereupon gave me strict instructions to go and see a well-known surgeon, who had already been told about me. Whatever he might decide I was not to let it worry me, as they were all anxious to help and I need not so much as think of the money question.

Afterwards I managed to get out to the hospital, where I met the Professor in a corridor. He was a tall, thin man of soldierly bearing, to whom I had always felt attracted. I had once described him in a short story as a real artist in his profession, and when he saw me he referred to this little incident.

'Well, well! So here's the culprit! They told me you wrote something about me. . . . What was it now? Some sort of a story, did they say? Well, it was a good one. That's the chief thing. What's your news to-day?'

Visitors

'If you're interested, doctor, I've brought you a well-developed tumour. A real collector's piece. I'll make you a special price, too.'

'Now look here, old man, I'm not even prepared to discuss the subject. You needn't look depressed. I mean, I can't say anything till you bring me a complete diagnosis. I want a plan like an engineer's drawing, to show me exactly where I am to open the skull—for, unless I am mistaken, it's in the head—and what I shall find if I do open it. It's just like sinking an artesian well. First, all those gentlemen with the divining rods must finish their job, then I come in with the trephine. Well, good-bye now!'

He gave me his dry, clever hand and gripped mine hard. Where did I remember having known that firm, decisive handshake, which made one feel a little ashamed and at the same time gave one confidence? Why yes, it was in my own short story, when he brings his hand from under the blanket and offers it to a disgruntled house surgeon.

It was with far lighter steps that I climbed the stairs on reaching home. I felt that I should not hesitate any longer, if Fate willed it that way. And yet I could not believe it. . . . For two days I had felt tolerably well and the ointment cure seemed to be proving effective. The chief thing was that, whatever happened, I should now know where to turn.

Meanwhile, however, the secret Parliament had cast its vote, and the result—although no one knew he was a member of the voting committee—proved quite different, and diverted my fate into another channel altogether.

I received a guarded intimation from the Gyulas. They had met, of course 'accidentally', and had had a 'chat' about me with our common friend and the surgeon I have already mentioned. The latter had spoken of his studies in America, where he worked as assistant to Cushing, the pioneer of modern brain surgery, with others of his best pupils. Cushing? Cushing? The name sounded familiar. Where had I heard of it? Aha! That amateur film I saw. . . . But what a coincidence! There, on the other side of that vast skull the globe, a man had been thinking about my own little skull and working to help it for the past thirty years, although he never so much as knew of its existence. Here, on this side, was I, looking in for half an hour at an amateur film show. Yes, yes, it *was* queer, but that wasn't the point just now. Then what was the point? Why, simply that they had written to America, in case. No, not in case I had to go to Boston, though I ought not to exclude that possibility altogether. But Cushing had a pupil in Stockholm. What was that? A pupil in Stockholm? Yes, in Stockholm—there was nothing to be alarmed about. It was just on the cards. Cushing had apparently declared his pupil to be at least as competent as himself. He operated only on the brain, and his equipment was one of the finest in the world. The fact was . . . they had written to him as well. M. used to know him in Boston. What, written already? Yes, they had written. . . . It was only a precaution and did not necessarily mean. . . . Hm, that was interesting. And the doctor in Stockholm—what was his name? Olivecrona, Herbert Olivecrona. Oliven? No, just Olive. Queer name, rather nice. It suggested a crown of olives or a garland of bays. It had a poetical sound about it, and that was enough for me. I began to imagine a tall man with Greek features. That was all very well, but it was entirely beside the point just now. Assuming I had to go, where was all the money to come from for such a journey? My publisher was very accommodating, but a situation of this sort had not been discussed between us, and now that I had consulted the Budapest doctor I would not dare to mention Stockholm to him.

Then things took an unexpected turn. The Upper House seemed to be intervening spontaneously in the deliberations of the Lower.

On the fifth day, though I had no idea to what I owed her visit, I had the pleasure of welcoming in my sick-room Countess ——, a member of one of Hungary's oldest and most distinguished aristocratic families. It was not this circumstance which made me glad to see her, but the fact that she is an intelligent, kind-hearted woman, and an old friend. We had tea together and chatted without any of the usual formalities of the sick-room. I soon realized that she knew exactly what was wrong with me. Her doctor, the famous surgeon, had explained my case to her in detail. I tried to pass the whole thing off as if it were an every-day matter.

Visitors

She looked at me in surprise. 'Don't you realize it isn't a joke this time? You're not a child, and I don't think you're a coward. I've come here on purpose to have a talk to you. It's very serious. You must be prepared to undergo an operation.' So she knew that, too? Yes, it appeared that she had spoken to the doctor, and knew that I might have to go to Stockholm. 'But——' I interposed. She cut me short. 'I've arranged all that. The whole thing's settled.' She mentioned the name of our most fashionable author, who had rung her up recently on the matter. She had also spoken to the Minister and to other people. (Unintentionally, she disclosed the fact that for days she had been giving her whole time to this problem.) Everything was now arranged, and I could have all the money I needed. It was curious how every one was in agreement on this point, the whole movement having been started by a bitter enemy of the man who was to continue it. From that moment, their mutual ill-feeling had vanished.

I could not speak. The jocular remarks I was preparing to make melted in tears. We shook hands without a word.

My emotion was somewhat tempered by a firm belief that it was all a matter of 'ifs' and 'assumings'. I had received no definite instructions as yet, and the very fact that people were so good and kind made me anxious to show them they had no cause for alarm, and that I could get myself out of this mess alone. The grey ointment was doing me good, and I had had no particularly disagreeable symptoms all day. I even felt like

141

pulling somebody's leg. They came to tell me that my friend Sándor, a brilliant writer who is one of my favourites amongst Hungarian stylists, had been inquiring after me on the phone. As I took up the receiver by my bedside I remembered somebody saying how sorry Sándor was to know of my illness, but he was afraid to call on me as he could not bear to see the 'hero bathed in his own precious blood'! 'Is that you?' I asked in a sepulchral tone, as if speaking from the grave. 'Sándor . . . old man . . . I'm . . . about . . . done for . . . done for now.' He could not find an answer, and I almost saw him turn pale at the other end of the line. Then, with a swift change of voice, I went on in a gay, bantering tone. 'It wasn't very nice of you, was it, not to go and see your old friend when you could? Incidentally, what's the news now?' He laughed, obviously relieved, and in five minutes he was round at my place, where we spent a most amusing time together.

Other visitors came in later to tea. The party was beginning to go with a swing just as Dr. R., the famous optician, walked in. 'Why, doctor, this *is* kind of you! Would you like me to send my visitors into the next room?' 'Well, if you don't mind—just for half an hour. I'd like to have a look at your fundus.'

The minutes seemed interminable as he directed the dazzling little lamp of the ophthalmoscope into my eye. I was beginning to fidget about in my impatience to tell him a funny story. At last it was over. With precise gestures he polished his instrument and replaced it in its case. Then he turned towards me, smiling and rubbing his knee. Thank God, I was going to hear some good news at last!

'Well, the papilla has again deteriorated by two and a half diopters, and there are signs of atrophy now.'

'Is that so?'

'As compared with the last changes, these have taken place in one quarter of the time.'

'But considering——'

'Just a moment, please. It is my duty as a doctor to inform you that if the tumour now growing on your brain is not removed within ten days, you will go permanently blind in three weeks. You understand me. Completely blind. Not a glimmer of light. . . .'

I said nothing, but he raised his hand, as if he had not yet finished what he had to say.

'Pardon me. That will be only the first symptom—complete blindness. A fortnight later, the others will begin in succession. First, complete paralysis. Then idiocy. And lastly——'

'Thank you. You needn't go on. I understand you, doctor.'

Somebody knocked. 'May we come in?' 'Why, yes! We're all ready now.'

And the gay throng came trooping back.

13

Death Tempts Me

This short chapter is by way of being an interlude or a dream. Perhaps it should be given in parenthesis, for it was in that way it happened—bracketed off, as it were, after the manner of dreams. To this day, I do not understand why it happened or what it signified. I give the story without comment.

The incident occurred on the following morning, two days before I left. At about ten o'clock I was told that a gentleman had called to see me. I gathered that he was a lecturer at some provincial or foreign university, but I had never heard his name. He was a young man, hardly over thirty, meticulous in dress and manner. He wore a perfectly cut suit in the best of taste. Only the lapels were perhaps a shade wider than is usual amongst intellectuals. The parting in his smooth hair was faultless. His grave, regular features seemed to serve the purpose of completing his dress, rather than vice versa.

In a modest, yet mildly patronizing tone, he explained to me that I should have known of his existence, had I been in a normal condition. We had met before, but it was quite understandable that I had forgotten him. He had heard from a mutual friend of ours that I was ill and had come to examine me, if I would allow him to do so. I did not dare to raise any objections, for I somehow gathered (though he did not say so) that he had been sent by the person to whom he had spoken of me.

Moreover, there was something strange about the whole conversation. He was as discreet and evasive as a Chinese diplomat, yet, oddly enough, I knew all about him in quarter of an hour, without being able to discover how much he knew about me. Whenever I questioned him on this point he said nothing, like a detective who is not permitted to reveal what he knows. I had never seen a doctor take the exalted, almost priest-like aspect of his calling so seriously. To every question he returned an evasive answer, or none at all. This, however, only if the question referred to me. Though he spoke of himself in an unassuming, guarded tone, I gathered that, despite his youth, he occupied a highly responsible post in the institution to which he belonged. He had plans for the future, and hoped to travel abroad with a scholarship for the purpose of studying a matter in which he took a professional interest.

After we had been talking for half an hour, I felt a miserable, insignificant, brainless worm. Although so young, my visitor seemed so much more learned and important a person than I that I felt like an ignorant

145   K

old peasant face to face with some high official. I could almost hear the official putting polite questions, but only giving such answers as he thought fit or as he considered the old rustic capable of understanding. I was also discouraged by my failure to make him smile, which at first I tried to do. Whenever I made a jocular remark his expression became a shade more serious than before. Behind this seriousness—and despite his peculiarly courteous and agreeable manners—I seemed to detect the conviction, which I found rather wounding, that an unbridgeable gulf lay between us. I was just a notorious humorist, while he was a man of science. We were living on different planets and there could be no question of our having interests, or even feelings, in common. I attributed my sense of inferiority to the fact that he was so much younger than I. Eventually, he returned to the object of his visit, with great delicacy but with a quiet decision of manner. If I had no objection, he would now examine me.

Once again I had to undress against my inclination. Then followed the various reflex tests that I knew by heart, but the young doctor went through them more solemnly—I would almost say more mysteriously— than the others. With him there were none of Professor R.'s nods and *ahems!* which had such a pleasantly reassuring or violently irritating effect on me, but which at least acted as a link between doctor and patient. He never, of course, made a remark of any kind.

Afterwards, the three of us sat on the divan—I leaning back and he rigidly upright—until my wife got up and began moving about the room. The doctor looked at his watch and he, too, rose to his feet.

'Well, at eight-thirty to-morrow morning——' he observed in a precise, official tone, but in a low voice, as if uttering some weighty, inescapable sentence, 'I shall have the pleasure of seeing you in operating theatre No. 4, at the S. clinic. I already have one or two things to do there.'

'*Me* d'you say? . . . To-morrow? . . . What for?'

'I just want to perform a little diagnostic test.'

He explained to my wife what it was all about, pointing out that his test would involve the use of surgical instruments. He wished to obtain a specimen of fluid *directly* from the place in my head where it was formed.

I was quite taken aback by the force of my indignation and by my instinctive impulse to rebel against his orders, but I took care not to let him see this. I tried to explain it to myself as mere repugnance at the thought of getting up early and leaving the house in my condition. I was ashamed to confess such qualms, and promised to be there in time.

Next morning, however, at nine o'clock, my wife appeared by my bedside in a panic.

'In Heaven's name, man! You aren't even up yet! They've been waiting for you in the operating theatre for the past half-hour!'

'I was as sound as a church. What's on, anyway?'

'Why, you made the appointment yourself!'

'So I did! I'd clean forgotten.'

'Well, get your things on at once.'

'What d'you think he'd say if I didn't turn up?'

'Are you scared?'

'Scared? Well . . . if it comes to that . . . maybe I am.'

'A little job like that!'

'Look here, I'll go to-morrow. He isn't leaving yet.'

'But *we're* leaving to-morrow.'

'Then I'll have it done in Vienna. I wish you'd leave me alone. We've got more important things to worry about.'

One day after my illness, when I could see to read again, I showed my wife a page in the leading neurological text-book, where this same diagnostic test was referred to as follows. I made no comment on it. 'The physician is warned against resorting to this test *before the final diagnosis*. Should the cyst be situated at the base of the cerebellum, the alteration of pressure causes it to be drawn into the *foramen ovale* and produces instant death, as was frequently observed before this fact became known.'

Two days afterwards, as I relate in the next chapter, I was informed that I had a large cyst at the base of the cerebellum, in the neighbourhood of the *foramen ovale*.

I did not see the young doctor again. Perhaps he never existed at all, and the whole story may have been of my imagining.

14

The Verdict

Ten more days . . .

And still there was no official diagnosis or indication. But nobody bothered now, even in my presence, to deny that the failure of the internal treatment left no room for doubt. Rapid decisions followed. I was no longer allowed to have visitors. Those who still called out of kindness were given my latest news in the passage. Sometimes I could hear their muffled whispering outside the door. My condition now became aggressively obvious. As if it had merely been waiting till it should receive a local habitation and a name, it no longer made any attempt to hide its seriousness from me. I had only one thought now. How could I lay my head on the pillow so as not to feel giddy? I could not recognize faces unless they came close to mine, but I was past worrying now.

I felt no inclination to ask for anything. From force of habit I scribbled a few words, but could not see what I had written, and each time I crumpled the paper in my hand. These notes were of little value in any case, for the ideas that occurred to me were banal enough. I wrote only insignificant, daily jottings, of a random and trivial nature. Not one of these had any bearing upon my life as a whole. This is a fact I have long recognized. Since I got over the happy, unconscious assumption of youth that life as a whole has some meaning independent of the days which compose it, I have not looked for more. There are only separate days of twenty-four hours—and twenty-four hours ought to be bearable somehow. Obviously, too, the last day of all. We have only to divide it up like the rest, when its turn comes.

Thanks to all the excitement and packing and comings and goings around me, the last twenty-four hours before I left were bearable enough. Foreign money—Austrian and Swedish—had to be bought and the route selected. We were to spend two days in Vienna, then pass through Berlin on our way to Malmö, Trelleborg, and Stockholm. A sixteen-hours' halt in Berlin was to give me my first glimpse of Germany under the Third Reich. My trunk proved to be still serviceable, and I only wanted a new suitcase, while my wife, who was coming with me, needed a few odds and ends. These included a hat-box, which she borrowed for the journey. I mention this hat-box because of all the discussions to which it gave rise. A whole legend grew up around the subject. Society split into two opposing camps, and there are still people who talk of it. Some were infuriated by the fact that she had even dreamt of borrowing such a thing. They considered that for a woman to accompany her dying husband across Europe with a hat-box was a cynical outrage to decency and good taste. I cannot share the view of those who were thus scandalized. In fact, I have a shrewd suspicion that if my wife had turned round and shot me while in an 'understand-ably' overwrought condition as the result of some violent scene, she would never have aroused so much righteous indignation as she then called down upon herself. 'Why?' I said, shrugging my shoulders, when some one again referred to it the other day in a disapproving tone. 'I suppose you'd have liked to see her pulling me along on a string, with her hat in one hand and my coffin under her arm.'

On the whole, I felt rather pleased with myself that last day. I managed to get through the preparations without any fuss or grumbling. I was careful not to make any 'unusual' or 'memorable' remarks that might afterwards suggest the observation, 'Yes, that's why he said it . . .' or, if the worst came to the worst, 'He must have had a presentiment. . . .' Already, I had begun to hope that I should come through that worst eventuality without any 'last words'. I have never thought much of these. To me, they seem like the last petal as we tear a daisy to pieces—'Yes, no, yes, no. . . . !' We fancy that the last 'Yes' or 'No' conveys a more essential message than the others, although it owes this entirely to the fact that there are no more to follow. I have on my conscience one piece of facetious-

ness in rather bad taste. Mihály's wife, the kindly
Ilonka, rang up to know when I was leaving. And
wasn't it going to be an expensive trip? 'The outward
journey', I replied, 'costs rather a lot. But they'll be
bringing me home with the luggage. And I'm told
urns don't pay duty.'

The Vienna express was to leave at eleven that
morning, and a small compartment had been reserved
for me where I could lie down. I refused help on the
way to the car, and supported myself by clinging to
the banisters. Our luggage was already stowed away.

Cini, Rózsi, and Pali accompanied us, Pali gazing
about him with intelligent curiosity. Rózsi, the good
soul, gave me an amulet, and, try as she might, could
not keep back her tears. Cini drew himself up proudly
when he saw her. As soon as I had dragged myself into
the car I offered him my hand. 'Well, Cini, old man,
look after the home. If, through no fault of mine, I
shouldn't come back to you . . . I'd advise you . . . just
a moment . . . what can I advise you to do? When
you're a man, let your beard grow. Perhaps, if you do
that, you'll earn more respect for yourself than your
father has done.' Cini smiled nervously, but said nothing. He blushed until his prominent ears were as red
as paprika. He reminded me vividly of some one. Who
could it be? Then I remembered that it was a four-
year-old photograph of himself.

A number of friends, most of them ladies, were waiting on the platform. They laughed and tried to en-

courage me—and all, God bless them, had brought some little offering to beguile my journey. Heaven knows that I have to thank women for all the unhappiness which has really counted in my life. Yet I wonder if this is true, after all? Whether it has been the case or not, what a good thing it is that there are women! No, I am not thinking of that. . . . In this human guise of ours, they are completely different beings from men and an everlasting promise that one day we may achieve some sort of goal. If God ever pardons the human race, it will be on account of them. Blessed Mary, pray for us!

We again put up at the Hôtel de France for a couple of nights. Next morning I humbly announced my arrival at the clinic. A few rapid tests were carried out. The optician no longer made any attempt to conceal his alarm. The papilla now showed seven diopters. Just as they anticipated. I was to come back first thing next morning and a letter to Stockholm would be waiting for me, so that I could leave at night by the sleeping-car of the Berlin express. Oh, but there was just one more little formality. They required a final piece of evidence to complete the series of documents which the Professor had used in making his report that morning. Would I mind stepping into the X-ray room for a moment? No, it was nothing to do with my head. They had all they wanted about that. As a pure formality, they wished to make an X-ray of my stomach.

The Verdict

An X-ray of my stomach? What was the idea? I racked my brains for an explanation, and was delighted when this occurred to me spontaneously. As soon as I found myself in the darkened room, with a shade suspended over my stomach, the problem solved itself. I might have guessed that the method of diagnosis by elimination would not be complete until they had excluded the remote possibility that the growth was of carcinomic origin, or, in other words, secondary and metastatic, for it is a curious fact that primary cancer never originates on the brain. In that case the operation on my skull would be a mistake. So there was nothing wrong, after all. . . . I don't know why, but I was convinced I had not got cancer. And the upshot was that they found no trace of it.

I spent the day in bed, not without a good deal of grumbling at the thought that I could not see my beloved Viennese streets. Early next morning I was in Pötzl's waiting-room. He had arrived before me, and was in consultation with the other doctors regarding my report. At that moment a curious interlude occurred. The door suddenly opened and Pötzl came in. It was the fourth time I had seen him in two weeks, but his manner seemed to suggest that it was not to be the last, for he had no papers in his hand. He came hurrying up to me.

'It won't be a minute,' he said encouragingly. 'It's almost ready. I just happened to think of one more thing. . . . D'you mind sitting down for a moment in this chair?'

The Verdict

I did so, and he leant over me. There were no instruments in his hand. He bent closer towards the back of my skull, as if he wanted to whisper something to me, though I knew that this was not what he intended. To this day, I cannot say from what deep well of childish memories the idiotic notion rose up in me that he was about to kiss my head, down at the back where I had 'a pain'. Then I realized that, all the time, he was forcibly pulling my ear about. He was listening, as he might have done to a patient's heart. Then he straightened his back and nodded.

'All right!' he said. 'We won't be a moment now,' and so hurried away.

Half an hour later, the committee came filing out with the Professor at its head. In his hand was a document. He did not give this to me, but laid it on the table in front of him. With a rather ceremonial air, he smilingly invited every one to take a seat. Then, in a courteous, pleasant tone, he began his explanations. From time to time, he glanced at me encouragingly. His manner could not have been more gracious, for it suggested that he looked upon us as equals—intelligent beings for whom the truth was of greater moment than life itself.

'All the reports concur,' he observed. 'Taken together with the last experiment, they indicate that a cyst, now approaching a hen's egg in size, is growing within a strictly circumscribed area on the right side of the brain, and at the back of the cerebellum. Behind or inside this cyst is what we call an angioma or congeries

155

of blood vessels. We have prepared a report on these lines which, if the patient wishes. . . .'

And then a strange thing happened. I felt that, in spite of my bad eyes, I was the only one who saw Pötzl struggling to keep his lips together. There could be no doubt about it—he was doing his utmost not to yawn! There he stood yawning in the midst of his report! How near I felt that gesture brought me to him! All of a sudden I understood him, and the sympathy I extended to him was as genuine as his for me. I had actually detected a yawn on the face of my respected colleague in the struggle against wickedness and stupidity! Don't smother it, I felt like shouting, don't be ashamed of that yawn! How well I knew it! It was the yawn that comes after some protracted piece of work that has been wearing, sleepless, inhuman. The same yawn has forced its way out just as I have caught sight of someone for whom I have been working and straining my energies, without hope of payment, gratitude, or recognition, perhaps only to see him turn against me and march contemptuously over my head. How much more deeply I was touched by that yawn as you passed sentence on me than I could ever have been by crocodile tears!

'Should the patient so decide,' he went on, as if nothing had happened, 'I shall place this report at the disposal of the surgeon selected by him.' He stood up, we all followed suit and he handed me the paper. 'Here you are, then. I have added a suggestion, naturally in the form of an alternative, to the report itself. I hear you want to go to Stockholm. If you decide to consult my distinguished colleague, be so kind as to remember me to him. And now good-bye, and the best of luck to you!'

We shook hands and he accompanied us as far as the corridor.

By now I knew something of the ultra-secret code in which doctors communicate with one another. I had become an initiate, and, on a bench in the street, I had the report read aloud to me. It was a highly instructive document. During the last century an artificial language was formed in connection with diagnosis and therapeutics, the etiquette of which bears a great resemblance to that of diplomacy. Although the letter was written to Olivecrona, it was not addressed to him personally or to any other surgeon, but to whichever representative of the Great Power, Surgery, should agree to receive it as an Ambassador sent by the other Power, Medicine. It began with a detailed and marvellously precise diagnosis. This had been arrived at with the help of a few obscure data, eked out by pure speculation, much as the physicist deduces with infallible accuracy from phenomena which always appear constant the one which has never yet been observed. Thus Le Verrier was able to calculate the mass and orbit of Neptune and the position where it should be looked for, from a consideration of certain irregularities noticed in the movements of other planets. Pötzl's authoritative diagnosis was followed by a cautious and tentative suggestion. Internal treatment having proved ineffective, something else must now be tried. There was a concluding observation. Should the surgeon think fit—'*Eventuell Operation*'.

'Operation may prove necessary.'

He had written 'may', though he knew very well that it was not a question of possibilities. If the patient were not to lose his life there was no choice in the matter. Nothing could save him then but the verdict of God, for he would be like the medieval criminal stripped naked to do battle with a knight in armour. The diplomatic etiquette of the two Great Powers was such that the neurologist could at the most advise the surgeon, but not tell him what to do.

For the last time, I strolled down the Alserstrasse under the old arches. I allowed myself to be led now, for I was coming more and more to resemble those mild fellow sufferers of mine—sheep afflicted with the staggers. Like them, I refused to walk straight and insisted on going round and round in a circle, as if I were turning about some invisible centre. As we strolled on my wife left me for a minute, propped up against the wall. I saw that she had run into the Church of Saint Anton, which we happened to be passing. When we had gone on a few steps, I asked her what she had promised the good saint if he spared my life. She seemed surprised, and it was quite evident that she had forgotten this little formality. I told her straight out what the saint would think of such empty-handed suppliants.

The Verdict

After lunch and apparently under the influence of the music that came filtering up from the hall, I dreamt the long dream which follows. I slept only from three till five and, on waking, I could not reconcile those brief hours of reality with the long duration of my dream.

15

The Place of a Skull
(Intermezzo)

With blinding light, the lustres
Flash in my clammy darkness. . . .
(From a poem of my youth.)

Yes, this was the same blinding light. It could not be
coming from anywhere but from the remote past of my
youth. As the daylight of my waking hours darkened
over in sleep, it shone ever more brilliantly. The music,
too, that came up from the hall was louder than at first,
and my ear blended it in dream with other sounds from
the old world of reality. Everything seemed keyed up
to the same pitch of excitement as on that evening
when, a boy of eighteen, I wrote the poem *At a Concert*. Yet this was no memory. It seemed rather as if the
past had come to life again. This time I had the impression that I was not at a concert, but at an opera. It was
probably the wedding march or the farewell ballad in
Lohengrin, or perhaps both at once. On the stage I

could see a throng of people in magnificent costumes. A triumphant *fortissimo* came thundering from the orchestra. The knight himself, in armour and white cloak, had not yet appeared on the stage. He could not very well do so, for he was sitting here in my place in the box, waiting for his turn. In fact, it seemed that I myself was Lohengrin, or at least the actor who was to play the part. I studied my make-up anxiously in a little mirror, with the nervous excitement that comes over me when I am about to give a lecture and am waiting to go on the platform. I should have gone on to it now, had I known what I had to say and had I not been barefoot, in spite of my magnificent costume. . . . If only, too, I had been able to collect my thoughts, for that monotonous, nasal whispering somewhere behind me in the darkness of the box kept on buzzing in my ear. . . . Why was he whispering like that? Whatever he was saying, I should not be able to hear the words because of the noise of the orchestra. Yet I had to be polite with him. I couldn't just tell him to stop, although they would be ringing any moment now for me to go on the platform and deliver my lecture. . . . But what was I to read from the clean sheets of paper on which I had forgotten to write something I ought to have written? After all, it wouldn't matter. The enthusiastic mood I was in would come to my rescue. . . . All the same, I needed to be careful, very careful. And besides, I couldn't back out of the whole thing now, as IT was there on the stage. Perhaps I had forgotten it during the first act. I had to try and find it, cautiously, so as not to be seen. I hoped it was there, I needed it to be there. It must be lying somewhere on the stage. Perhaps they had pushed it aside, but it couldn't have rolled off without my noticing it. It might be a good thing, after all, that I had bare feet. During my lecture I could feel for it with my toes. I knew I should recognize it, because it was soft and rubber-like to the touch. It couldn't be larger than a hen's egg or a little ball. I began to feel for it stealthily under the table. If I found it, I should have to filch it away or else crush it under my foot. But what in God's name was I to do if it wasn't there? Or if they had really rolled it down into the orchestra? I might go after it there, but I should never, never find it. . . .

And this apparently was what had happened. Otherwise, what should I be doing here in New York for the first time in my life? A clue had led me here, poor, unhappy detective that I was, from the town where I had been Lohengrin. That might have been Budapest, Vienna, or Berlin—I had no idea which, but this I recognized as New York. Elsewhere, I shouldn't have felt so violently sick as I did now in this little room on the fiftieth floor of a skyscraper. The room was continually swaying to and fro but, although I found this disagreeable, it did not alarm me, as I knew it was usual for skyscrapers to rock about. I was negotiating with a great, hulking, sallow-skinned fellow who had an overbearing, yet suave manner. I knew quite well that he was Al Capone or some one of the same kidney, but we didn't let on to each other who we were. We were giving no secrets away. It was important to be very tactful and we talked of the *thing* in an evasive, roundabout way, like diplomatic crooks. I sat theorizing and chattering, while he looked at me superciliously and said hardly a word, as if he had it in his possession and was letting me waste my breath for nothing. Of course he had it. He had stolen it and was keeping it somewhere in a strong-box. He hadn't destroyed it, but was preserving it carefully. And, all the time, the rascal would pretend we were talking about the Lindbergh baby. He made out that he did not see any contradiction between my talking about a tumour and he about a baby. Of course, we were both using circumlocutions, but it was perfectly obvious that when I spoke of a palpable and clearly circumscribed formation that was in no way carcinomic, this could not possibly mean a baby. Yet he persisted in saying it was a baby, although as it was not at all like the Colonel, it couldn't be his. It began to get on my nerves that I kept saying 'tapping', because it worried me that this was not the word I wanted. It was no use. The word 'kidnapping' simply wouldn't come. He was the only one who knew it, but he did not help me out. I made a desperate attempt to win him over by offering to show him the beauties of the Hungarian language. I quoted poems, and even sang feelingly to him. He thereupon poured out some brandy, which meant that he had no more to say on the matter. He was not prepared to discuss the question any further or to give me a clue. We clinked glasses with a flourish, but the brandy had no taste.

Nor was there any taste in these exotic delicacies they were offering me in Ankara (for I was in Ankara now) at a banquet in my honour, and not much of a banquet, either. There were only four or five of us in the bar of a little tavern. It was the Balkans with a vengeance. I could find no taste in the food, though I kept eagerly swallowing *pilaf* and other stuffed dishes. There were also sausages and a queer, rubber-like substance that was meat and yet sweet to the palate. I chewed and chewed, but could get no taste out of them and my stomach remained empty. Luckily, the editor of the local paper, who wore a red fez, made friends with me and invited me out with him. We walked stealthily along tortuous alleys, and I was delighted to see that Ankara was exactly like Venice. This encouraged me to walk boldly on. And then the mysterious women of the night began to steal past me—marvellous, snake-like figures clothed in romantic silks. I quickened my steps and at last caught up with one of them. Her alluring form stimulated my senses. I bent eagerly over her, but her face was hidden by an accursed veil. I could see only her eyes sparkling. We walked side by side for a short distance, while I whispered to her, waiting till I should feel in the mood for her. Soon, I realized that the mood was long in coming. The woman, too, was rather insipid. Under the gleam of a lantern I impatiently pulled down her veil. Afterwards, we went on talking

for a while, but the conversation was dull and common-
place. I knew that this was the end of it all. The
woman looked like a sister of mine who died some years
ago of an intestinal tumour. I spoke to no one else,
because I felt sure that, under the veils, they would all
resemble her.

But that was not what I wanted. I had something
else to do, and, besides, this wasn't Ankara now. I was
in an old Spanish museum somewhere, perhaps in
Madrid or Seville, or it might even be the Alhambra
itself. In fact, it was the Alhambra. But how oddly
everything was arranged! Antiquities, natural history
specimens, weapons, minerals and pictures were all
mixed up together in a confused jumble. I revelled in
all this disorder, for I could forage about without being
disturbed even by the attendant. I opened some of the
chests and rummaged about amongst the silks and fine
materials. I took out books and dusty manuscripts, and
laid them on my desk. . . . The thought had been worrying me for years that I ought to tidy up my bureau and
the drawers of my writing-desk. Now was the time to
get to work on it, for the job must be undertaken at last.
I fished out some of my school exercise books. . . . Then
what should I come upon but the pressed flowers I
used to be so proud of, because of the pale pink ane-
mone between its fine white sheets of blotting-paper?
There were anemones and other plants with intricate
red or blue veining. . . . Yet now I saw that they were
not my pressed flowers, after all. I was bitterly dis-

appointed, for it had been a great joy to find them again. They were not the pressed flowers, yet, all the same, I was glad to have found this book, for I thought that it, too, was lost. I was looking at Szobota's anatomical atlas, and what I had taken for plants was a coloured diagram of the vascular system in all its complexity. I could see even the pulsation of the blood, so delicate was the workmanship. It seemed to be made of a network of thin glass. It was actually throbbing, and here and there the blood vessels were gathered into congeries. . . . I had found the atlas now, but where was . . . ? Where had they put that——? I felt I should again have to go through all the various cases and the minerals and the weapons. . . . It must be somewhere there. If only the attendant didn't come back! Time was slipping away, and still I saw nothing but pictures and yet more pictures. It seemed to be an art collection. Yes, it must be that, for I recognized one of the pictures as a Goya. My heart almost beat faster as I realized that I was looking at the original. There could be no doubt about it—I knew the picture well. It was called 'The King's Orchard', and the canvas showed an enormous oak-tree in the centre, from the branches of which men were hanging by the hundred, pitiably wasted in the dry rigidity of death.

A shiver ran down my back. I did not dare to look this hanging man in the face, yet I knew that I had to do so. I had to look at him while he was still alive and gasping like a dying fish. I had to look at him because I was to write about it for next morning's paper. The

166

article had to be ready by nine o'clock. It was too ghastly—I couldn't do it. I had been told not to write it in any other way than as it actually happened. Then, for an instant, I felt an immense sensation of relief. Perhaps it wasn't real—perhaps, after all, I was dreaming! The whole thing was nothing but a dream. A dream all that tortured detective hunt across the world! A dream my search for the tumour! There wasn't any such thing and I need not look for it, after all. There was no hanging man. I had not to write about him or to look him in the face. . . . No longer afraid, I loitered for a few minutes amongst the crowd in that vast, strange hall. Whatever happened now, I knew it was only a dream, and I might wake up at any moment. I did not even hurry, for this other foreign town interested me, though it was growing rather cold.

But I did not wake up and I soon forgot that I was dreaming. I was walking round and round now, trembling and anxious, in the midst of the crowd. I couldn't speak Russian, and these people didn't understand German. That was a great pity, for at last I had tracked it down and was within sight of my goal. Although they did not understand my words, I could see from my gestures and from the tone of their voices that they were talking about *it*. This meeting had been called to settle the matter once and for all. The speaker on the platform was talking about it. The harsh Slav words, borne to me on the wind, were like the cracking of a whip. It was no good. I should never be able to speak, for nobody would understand me. A crowd of ragged bystanders with prominent cheek-bones leered at me sarcastically. I could not explain to them, but if only they knew that I was the one they were talking about, that the whole revolutionary meeting had taken place in connection with me and that the hanging was not the important thing but the announcement that it existed and that the class-conscious proletariat had discovered the hidden treasure and was now taking possession of it. . . . My temples were throbbing and I began to stamp impatiently with the cold. 'Move along, there, move along! That fellow's said his say!' The crowd, now unruly and turbulent, began to move away from the square. We passed in front of the Kremlin and poured into the side-streets, while groups of people kept disappearing behind the doors. The crowd wavered and some of the people stopped to argue, saying we ought not to go in that direction, for they had taken it to the old Parliament. Others declared it was a matter for the Central Committee and that they had certainly handed it over to the Palace. It flashed into my mind that I hoped we would not have to go into the notorious cellars of the GPU. I felt nervous, as we began to feel our way down some steps. There were three of us now—a great, hulking coalheaver in a beret, Vedres, from the freethinking Circle of Galileo, who was to die of influenza, and myself. Vedres was explaining everything with a superior, knowledgeable air. I trusted only him, for he had lived here for twenty years, and knew more than the others. The tumour had been carried to the office, but, of course, it had to be registered in the books. We had only to trust ourselves to Vedres and he would lead us in through the secret doors in five minutes' time. We were already standing in front of an iron door. They would let us in at once now and I should see it—but still the door did not open. Vedres cursed and raged. They had shut at twelve and nothing could be done about it, as they would not open for business till next day. Unless . . . unless we went to an office where there was a permanent service. He knew a man called Sergejelev who worked there and who might be able to arrange for us to get in that day. . . . I had the feeling, however, that we were caught in the labyrinths of bureaucracy and that we should never find what we were looking for.

Or had I already found it? It seemed that now my problem was where to hide the thing in some absolutely secret place. How was I to get rid of it? Whoever would guess that in the heavy, shapeless parcel I had been trailing about with me for days, I was hiding the world's largest diamond—twenty times the size of the Koh-i-noor or the Orlov—wrapped up like a melon in old newspapers? Of course, I should never be able to sell it. They would say it was just a fine piece of glass, and no one would ever believe that it was a diamond. I couldn't break it up, because I hadn't the necessary instruments. It was of no use to anybody, and I had no idea what to do with it. I had tried to get rid of it by 'accidentally' putting it down and leaving it behind, but they always brought it back to me. I stood looking round cautiously. Would any one see me if I dropped it in the canal? Yes, there they were, watching on the other bank. In despair I dragged it along with me again.

I was sick and tired of it all. By now, every one had gone home and the streets were empty. Not only the whole town seemed dead, but the woods and the open country as well. The moon was swinging round in great circles and the music had stopped. This was the Outer Space beyond the Milky Way of which I had read in Arrhenius, with its incandescent mists and spiral nebulae. So I must be looking at the Expanding Universe. . . . But if it was expanding, it must be getting continually larger and flying ever more swiftly apart. Where, then, was I to lay down my burden or find what I was looking for, assuming, as seemed probable, that it was no longer subject to gravitation?

And then came many more cities and lands and incandescent mists and spiral nebulae. . . .

At last, I heard myself say a word aloud, articulating it clearly, so as not to forget it. I was going up for an examination which might be fixed for to-morrow, and I did not know the chairman of the board of examiners. Luckily, I remembered the subject in which I was to be examined. 'Sk—ull,' I said, very distinctly.

And now long files of people were coming up with skulls in their hands. They rolled them down into the valley, where they piled up in heaps, some of which were soon as high as the hill itself. I gave a satisfied nod, like a good student who knows he is not to be caught out. 'The place of a skull,' I explained in a whisper for the benefit of a candidate whom I could not see, and who was inadequately prepared for the examination. 'Golgotha,' I added, to show off my learning.

Yes, that was it, friend Al Capone—Golgotha, and not 'tapping' or even 'kidnapping'!

I knew that I had only to give a cry now and I should wake up in earnest. I was lying on my spine, and it was hurting me. I couldn't bear it any longer. . . .

16

The Die is Cast

M_y dream must have been a fairly long one as measured by external time, for it was growing dark when I woke up. I felt giddy and dazed, and began stumbling about to collect my things. We had three hours in front of us, the Berlin train being due to leave at nine o'clock sharp. I was to have a sleeping compartment to myself. My wife had arranged to relieve me of responsibility for the customs examination during the night, so that I could remain undisturbed till morning. It was April 28th. Keen, biting little winds went whistling through the Wienerwald. I expected this nip in the air to get sharper as we advanced. Being a child of the kindlier south-east, I had never ventured into the far north of Europe, but my education was just able to tell me that they were not yet through with winter there. This reminded me that I had to buy a Jaeger shirt, if there were still any shops open. I ought to have mentioned it yesterday. Tickets, visas, money—had we got everything? Yes, it was all ready now and the Bandi Gáspárs were waiting downstairs in the hall, so we had to make haste. There was nothing left to do except to go and have dinner in an attractive little restaurant on the Ring. Meanwhile, our luggage was to be put on the train and I was to drive straight from the restaurant to the station. (This idea frightened me somewhat. I found taxis particularly trying, as I had no chance to lie down in them, and my head felt like a hastily packed suitcase in which all the contents had come undone and were sliding about in hopeless confusion.)

The Gáspárs were cheerful and kind. Kató told us proudly that she had nearly finished her translation of Móricz's *Transylvania*, and that it would make a huge volume in German. Bandi, however, kept looking furtively at the time. 'What's the matter, Frici? Something wrong?' 'No, nothing. It's going to be quite all right. Do I look so bad?' 'No, not that. Only. . . .' I did not need to be told that I was feeling rather downhearted. Perhaps because it was evening and it would soon be night. Had we been due to leave in the morning I should have felt much more lively. But it was nightfall, and there was a howling wind. Nightfall—and in this cold I was setting out for the north. The Ossianic effect was one too many for me. I thought of a line from the Hungarian poet Arany, 'Where art thou, Homer, with thy light-filled sky?' That sky I might never see again. . . . There came into my mind a poem called 'The Northern Lights' which I had written long ago and in which there was a sad presentiment that, in the end, everything would go northwards amongst the ice and snow, whither all the world's compasses are pointing.

> *Northwards, ever northwards*
> *The iron finger turns,*
> *Not to be deflected*
> *By any sun that burns*
> *On azure seas, reflected*
> *From wave or coral bar,*
> *Northwards, ever northwards,*
> *Following its star. . . .*

'Well, good-bye, good-bye!—Yes, yes!—We'll soon be back. . . . Wait a moment, children! Let me sit by the driver, will you? All right, I'll manage by myself. You needn't hold my arm. . . .'

Only the faithful Jóska came with us to the station. I was glad that some one would be there. Those Viennese stations were hateful—dirty, smelly, and sad. It was always cold and always raining. And how wretchedly ill-lit they were! And how the porters shouted up and down the place! I could not bear this or the sight of Jóska's melancholy face. I realized that I needed some one to joke with, not because I felt in the mood just then, but quite the contrary. I turned to it as I might have done to opium. Jóska and I went for a stroll beside the line, and I began to pull his leg. 'Being kind to your friends isn't much fun, is it? Just think what a fine life it would be if you were sitting with Gusterl in front of a steaming cup of tea at the

The Die is Cast

Café Bastei . . . ! You needn't be afraid. It'll be quite different when I get back from Stockholm. Like the dream I was telling you about—you remember? I shan't be . . . quite fit . . . but, of course, the operation will have been a success. I'll still be in the convalescent stage, you know. The first thing we'll do when I get back will be to go and see Pötzl. It'll take a bit of doing, I admit. . . . I shan't be quite myself again yet, as I was saying. . . . You'll see me scramble up the clinic staircase on all fours. . . . On my knees, don't you know? I'll have to have brushes on my hands like the legless beggars you see in the street. Pötzl will come out to meet me very politely, making out that he sees nothing queer in it at all. He'll welcome me back in his kind, sugary way. "Ach, ach! Freut mich sehr, also gut gelungen? Gratuliere. . . ." "Jawohl, Herr Professor, vorläufig aber, wie Sie sehen. . . ." Then he'll answer like a flash, "Ja, ja, sind noch einige Schwierigkeiten, es wird schon . . . es kann noch vielleicht. . . ." After that, there'll be a moment of painful silence, before we start talking of other things. Then I'll say good-bye to him politely, and start scrambling down the stairs on my brushes.'

By now, Jóska was looking the world in the face once more. He gave a low gurgle, and all was well again. There was no longer any need for him to try and look sympathetic or to think of 'appropriate' messages for me. It was just 'Good-bye, good-bye!'—and we were off.

I went straight to my sleeper, where I was comfort-

The Die is Cast

able as soon as I lay down, for I did not feel the jolting so much in this position. It would have been delightful to have some one come and read to me then, so that I could just lie thinking of nothing, but, fortunately, I was well supplied with sleeping draughts, and when I woke up the horizon was already growing grey. The hardest part of the journey was over now, and we had crossed the frontier into the new Germany. It was a strange sensation to be returning in this way after twenty-five years. How young I was in those days—hardly twenty-three! How ardent and tragic and how mad! To Berlin I brought my first wife, the passionate actress with velvet eyes. I had abducted her romantically from her husband, hurrying her away, revolver in hand, past the dark boxes and trap-doors of the theatre. For six months we lived secretly near Berlin in the beautiful new district of Freidenau. We felt that eternal life was just beginning for us, and we used to stand on our balcony talking of the stars. How fresh Germany was then, how full of audacity and enterprise and preparation! I remember one could have a six-roomed flat rent free for three years in the new suburban districts, if one took it on a six years' lease. From there I used to send tragic and humorous stories home to Budapest. With shouts of joy I discovered the great city. 'Berlin is feeding!' I cried one day ecstatically, at the sight of the crowd eating *belegtes Brötchen* in Aschinger's sandwich-palace. I might have been sending home reports on the progress of a baby. This time Germany seemed to me more serious and more restrained. Her Renaissance did not appear as gay or light-hearted as her birth had been. I noticed few new buildings, although I had expected to see them everywhere. At last, on an unpretentious little house not yet completed my eye caught the following inscription: *We could never have built this without our Führer*. I could not help thinking of the schoolboy joke. 'I say—I'm letting them build that new house.' 'You? How d'you make that out?' 'Well, they're building it—and I'm just letting them.' I saw no other evidence of the change that had taken place.

At lunch time we reached the outer station in Berlin. My wife went on to the hotel opposite, while I stayed behind to shave. I had assured her that I would be quite capable of finding the hotel by myself, though I soon realized that her confidence in me had been misplaced. I succeeded in shaving after a fashion, but afterwards I lost my bearings completely. As I tottered towards the exit it became obvious that I was incapable of walking straight. My feet kept turning inwards, and I found it distinctly amusing to see how I kept looking straight in front of me, yet *walking in a circle*; just like a sheep with the staggers, I said to myself triumphantly. I welcomed this occasion to test by experiment the *dual nature* of the body and the mind, in which I have always believed. Although I was fully conscious, thinking clearly, and experiencing normal sensations, my body refused to obey orders—or, if it obeyed orders, they were not mine. They might have been given by some one else lurking inside me. It seemed that *my body had a mind apart*, independent of 'me', and that this mind was now in revolt and stirring up the body to rebel against me.

The situation was decidedly comic. It had a peculiarly German, *Fliegende Blätter* style of humour, admirably suited to my surroundings. The external world was not slow to take part in the comedy. As I struggled to reach one of the exits, either by walking sideways or any other way I could, a uniform loomed up in front of me. 'Bitte, die Fahrkarte!' With the best will in the world I could not give him the ticket, because my wife had taken it with her. I dragged myself helplessly towards another exit. 'Bitte, die Fahrkarte!' There was no escape here, either. The incident was repeated five times, until I had painfully made the circuit of the entire hall. I was far too tired to argue or offer explanations. My fate appeared to be sealed, for even if I had been able to walk straight they would never allow me to go through. A kind of gravitational attraction held me like a planet, doomed to revolve for ever in the same orbit around the walls. After half an hour, when I was beginning to lose all hope, my wife succeeded in finding me. She had been searching for me in despair, and had no idea what could have happened. She confessed to a suspicion that I had bolted into one of the trains to escape the operation that awaited me in Stockholm. She had the tickets with her. Holding my head proudly, I marched out of the prison in which I had so completely lost my

sense of direction that I could never have got out
alone.

I refused my lunch, on the pretext that the eels were
too greasy. Afterwards I tried the experiment of writing a letter without seeing the words. I succeeded
fairly well. All I needed was a little practice. Once my
fingers acquired the knack, they would not need eyes
to guide them. We could all write with our eyes shut
if they were to invent some simple plastic device for
keeping to the lines. I ought to take out a patent for
it. . . . I wrote to Matter-of-Fact Gyula and Absent-
Minded Gyula, to Cini and the Countess. I heard afterwards that my letters were quite legible.

After I had several times renewed my acquaintance
with the wash-basin by retching over it, even that grim
afternoon came to an end at last. My train was leaving
at eleven o'clock for Trelleborg, which was already in
Scandinavia. Like a fidgety child, I kept on asking to
walk once more down the Unter den Linden, now that
I was in Berlin again. We therefore set out to trudge,
slowly and painfully, along the Friedrichstrasse. Luckily for us, it was a Sunday. We could see nothing in the
shop windows, as the shops themselves were closed. Ah,
there was the Café Kerkau—so I recognized it, after
all! How many times had I sat up there on the first
floor with Etel Judik of the violet eyes! 'Zwei Melange,
schön!' and the head waiter would hurry away, while
we buried ourselves in the newspapers. What news

179

there was from the great world—Paris, London . . . !
'Look at this, darling! You see? It's the real thing this
time. There's no catch in that. The photo shows him in
the air. . . . It's Blériot's aeroplane! He came to Budapest last year. The paper says he was up in the air for
a whole hour the other day! I tell you, we shall soon be
flying. . . . It's not a car we'll get when we're rich, but
an aeroplane!' 'Yes, all right, but I just want to read
something here. There's a terrible new illness broken
out in Spain—a kind of fatal influenza. . . .'

The Trelleborg express was a smart, aristocratic-
looking train. Our sleeper was small but splendidly
equipped. I thought I heard something about crossing
the sea, but my head felt muzzy and I was sure I had
made a mistake. How could a train cross the sea, or
were they talking about a bridge of some kind? I tried
to go to sleep quickly, for we were to arrive at six
o'clock in the morning. Already, there was a nip in
the air.

I woke up with the impression that the train was
rocking about underneath me. Was it an earthquake
or another attack of giddiness? I pulled myself out of
bed and lifted the blind. Instead of the horizon and the
livid night sky I saw a wall of red iron in front of the
window. I shuffled out into the corridor in my pyjamas
and slippers. The iron wall seemed to curve in under
the footboard, and the wheels were not moving. In
spite of this, the train was rolling from side to side. I got
out and walked a few steps out of the tunnel into which

the train had been run. We were on a giant ferry-boat. Sea and sky formed a single black mass, with only a few buoys shining here and there. Far away in the distance—for the horizon always seems wider at night—was a row of twinkling lights. A sailor leaning over the side of the ship answered my whispered question in a foreign tongue. We talked in low tones, for every one was asleep on the boat and in the train. He spoke one of the Scandinavian languages, and I did not understand him. Then he pointed to the distant row of lights. 'Köpenhamn!' he exclaimed. 'Ah, Kopenhaven!' I understood him as soon as I had changed his soft Swedish syllables into the harsher sounds of German. After a few moments I gathered from him that we had been at sea for two and a half hours, and that we should reach Trelleborg punctually at six o'clock. I climbed back into my bed, but could not get off to sleep again.

A cold, bleak morning by the seashore. This iron world of ships and jetties, cranes and girders—why did it all seem so familiar to me? Of course—I had seen it in the paintings of Whistler! It was another case of reality being anticipated by the vision of genius.

Get on, get on! I wanted to say, for by now I was heartily sick of the journey. I no longer cared about anything. This was not how I had pictured my first journey to the north. The railway station, thank God, was beside the quay. A little train was to take us as far as Malmö, an hour and a half's run. There we were to

The Die is Cast

change into the Stockholm express. As we entered our compartment I realized how foreign everything looked. Instead of seats there were great, deep arm-chairs of the kind one sees in Hungary by the fireplace in old country houses. Our train took us through a bright green countryside. The air was soft and fragrant, and as pure as if it had been newly washed. Everything looked green, for most of the trees were pines, but in places a little snow lingered on the hill-tops.

At Malmö we changed trains. We took our breakfast in the dining-car, which made a charming little restaurant. The cashier, a blonde Solveig, smiled amiably to me from her pay-desk at the side. I remembered I had to call her *Fröken*. The waiter recommended us to take a *smörgåsbord*. This was the first time I heard the name of a dish which was to be the chief item on my menu for six weeks. I expected it to be a kind of hors-d'œuvres, and I was horrified to see them put before us a selection of at least forty dishes. In the midst of pink, blue, and green fish, roast meats and minces, there was an immense silver bowl of cream. Unfortunately, I could find no taste in any of them (as in my dream of two days before), and only in the case of one fish did I realize that its flavour was sweet. It could not very well be otherwise, having been prepared with strawberry jam.

The train was gliding on between pine forests—dark green yielding to pale green, then dark green again. Already we had completed a good part of the fourteen-hour journey. Pine trees, blue lakes, an everlasting succession of red-painted wooden houses—such is Sverige, a naïvely romantic land of hills and babbling streams and dim blue waters, overhung by trees, with red farmsteads nestling amongst the rocks. A land that smiles as simply and with a charm as cool and gracious as a village bride.

I was worn out by the time our train rumbled into the capital at about three o'clock. I could just make out that we were by the seaside, and that we were running between canals and waterways. I saw the light of a glittering tower—the golden dome of the Town Hall. For the moment that was all that Stockholm meant to me, and it was all that it was to mean for another four weeks. We were met at the station by Mrs. H., who had been informed of our arrival from Budapest. They bundled me into a car, but I saw nothing of the drive except asphalt pavements. I felt at the end of my tether. Nothing appealed to me any more. We stopped in front of a clean, white staircase. On the façade I could just read in black letters, 'Serafimer Lasarettet'. They helped me up the stairs which I knew I was not to come down for a long while—if ever. I was shown into a simple private room leading off the corridor. Two tall nurses in white caps took charge of me, undressed me, and put me to bed. They took away my medical reports.

The Marathon runner had delivered his message.

17

My Prisons

Silvio Pellico, the lovable author of *Francesca da Rimini*, once wrote a book with the unpretentious title *My Prisons*. At the beginning of last century he spent ten years as a prisoner of the Emperor Francis in the Italian provinces of Austria and at Spielberg. This book has always attracted me because of the serene detachment with which he describes his superhuman sufferings, as if he claimed no more than to be regarded as a modest expert in the chains and prisons of reaction.

Since this book of mine is in the nature of a fantastic romance (for the reality of Europe in the twentieth century seems to me an adventure surpassing the wildest flights of imagination), I may perhaps be allowed to borrow an elementary symbolical device from the old story-tellers. I shall accordingly claim to regard as ten years those ten months of my life of which it is my object to describe the most interesting—namely, the first three. In my sick room at the Serafimer Lasarettet, I often thought of Silvio Pellico. I would try to calm my unruly spirit by remembering how patiently he must have submitted to his fate. In his case destiny used the Emperor Francis as its tool, whereas in mine it had chosen a malignant tumour. I came to understand that I had nothing to do but to await events and to observe what was going on in me and around me, without making any sentimental notes in the margin. On this occasion, for the first time in my life, I was to observe not for the sake of recording that personal vision which the artist calls 'truth' and which ceases to exist with the brain that perceives it, but for the sake of *reality*, which remains reality even if we have no means of communicating its message. Never had I been so far from a lyrical state of mind as in this, the most subjective phase of my life.

My wife had taken a room at the Cosmopoliten Pension in the Nybro-Gatan. She came to the hospital every morning at about ten o'clock and remained till late in the afternoon. From her I picked up a little information about the town in which I was living, and of which I knew less than I did of Tokyo. From my bed I could see the stately tower, surmounted by a golden dome, which sang hourly of the flight of time in dignified, melodious tones. This was my only link with the notion of time, for my red watch, whose hands I could not see in any case, had gone wrong, and one tends to be economical abroad. The doctors treated my wife most courteously as a colleague. On the first day she told me that the Professor had invited her to watch him operate, and had shown great kindness in explaining the cases to her.

That first day nobody even mentioned my imminent operation. From the moment of my arrival I lay in a mood of sluggish indifference, waiting to be laid on the operating table at any moment. I asked for a sleeping draught, and no longer cared what happened. Next day I awoke at six o'clock. Two white-capped nurses then came into the room, washed me and changed my sheets. To do this, they lifted me up and, while one of them held me in mid air, the other changed the bedclothes with deft fingers. Neither of them spoke German. At eight the charming Sister Kerstin appeared, bringing with her some scent, a smile, and eggs, cheese and butter for breakfast. She spoke German and English well, and from her I learnt that I was not to be operated on for the time being, but that I had first to be examined like any other patient entering the hospital. When I told her of the exhaustive diagnosis I had brought with me she replied that the examination was *de rigueur*. All reports were politely and respectfully consulted, but none could exempt a patient from being examined on the premises. Then was there still a chance that I might not have to be operated on after all? 'If the Professor doesn't think it necessary,' answered Sister Kerstin, 'why should they operate?'

After breakfast, which I had the utmost difficulty in swallowing, I took stock of my cell. I was lying in a clean, but very plain little room. It was only when I needed something that I realized how modern and practical its equipment was. The bed table opened on all four sides, the bed itself was on wheels and could be raised as required, and on the wall behind me was a pair of earphones for the wireless.

At ten o'clock Dr. Söjkvist looked in during his rounds, bringing with him a German doctor. I was extremely glad of his company. He spoke several languages fluently and was a man of truly European outlook, with a keen sense of humour and a mind quick to respond to the most recondite allusions. He had travelled extensively and had visited Budapest. It amused me to hear him try and pronounce the name Márgit-sziget. Our paprika chicken came in for a word of praise, but he thought Hungarian soups too greasy. We hardly referred to my illness, for most of our time was spent in exchanging jokes, as if he had called to see me on a friendly visit. He looked surprised when I came over sick and leant towards the basin. 'I seem to have a bad effect on you,' he said in an almost offended tone. 'I'd better be going. . . .'

Fröken Kerstin opened the door. She was accompanied by a tall attendant, who fixed a bar under my bed and began to wheel me along. The bed moved out into the corridor, along the ground floor, into a lift and thence down into the basement. After wheeling me from end to end of the latter, they stopped in front of a door from which the attendant read a word aloud in reply to my Crusoe-gestures. 'Ögon.' Recognizing the German word *Augen*, I realized that my tests were

187

about to begin all over again. I sighed, knowing what I was in for, like an old soldier who has been in the trenches before. I knew that I should have to wait my turn, then to sit for a long while bolt upright, to watch for the light signals and to endure the glare of the mirrors. I was placed beside a bed in which a thin, intelligent-looking girl was lying. She had the fair hair I was now becoming familiar with. She was obviously nervous, and I saw her trying to get up in the bed. I wanted to reassure her, but, alas, I knew no Swedish. From the next room came an international sound which is understood everywhere—the crying of a child, frightened, no doubt, by the dazzling mirror. My neighbour and I both looked in the direction from which the sounds came. I smiled and she did the same, or at least I fancied I saw her smile. By now, I had learnt to interpret every hint afforded by the shifting of light and to complete the general effect from memory. I was getting used to this strange semi-darkness in which I lived, and I almost began to like it. I could still see the outline of figures fairly well, and my imagination supplied the details, like a painter filling an empty frame. I tried to form a picture of any face I saw in front of me by observing the person's voice and movements. People were often astonished to see that I could not distinguish between colours and shades, yet I would catch momentary facial expressions unnoticed by those with normal eyesight. I, too, was surprised. The idea that I might already have gone blind struck me with sudden terror. What I fancied I saw was perhaps no more than the

My Prisons

stuff that dreams are made on. I might only be using
people's words and voices to reconstruct the lost world
of reality, just as our mind, at the moment we fall
asleep, forms images resembling those of real life from
the *phosphenes* that dance before our closing eyes. I
stood on the threshold of reality and imagination, and
I began to doubt which was which. My bodily eye and
my mind's eye were blending into one, and I could no
longer be certain which of the two was really in control.

I felt, rather than saw, the gloomy atmosphere of
those subterranean rooms. They lifted me this way and
that, placed me in strange-looking chairs, the disks
revolved, and the blazing lamp shone in my face again.
They plied me with questions, which I obediently
answered. Here I was just a 'case' and nothing more.
The young doctor who carried out the test had certainly never heard my name. For him it had absolutely
no associations, whether good or bad. His feelings towards me would depend entirely on my behaviour
now. I tried to give him precise answers, and did not
say a word more than the question required. When,
however, I ventured to ask him what he had found, he
looked at me with an expression of pained surprise.
What had that to do with a common or garden 'case'?
He assured me a little ironically that he had put it all
down in his report, then nodded for them to bring in
the next patient.

It was twelve o'clock by the time they wheeled me
back along the winding corridors. I had been living

here only for twenty hours, and yet what a comforting, home-like sensation it was to see the door of my own room again! Home—a purely relative idea if ever there was one! No doubt the microbe clinging to a bullet in mid air looks upon the projectile as home as we look upon this old globe. To me, the room I recognized was now home, though it was far away in a northern country of which I had as yet seen nothing. I found myself wondering if I should ever see it at all now, and thereupon made a desperate effort to think of something else.

Home to me now was not even the room but the bed, and not even the bed, but just the hollow that I had made for myself to lie in comfortably when I turned over on my side at the approach of nausea or giddiness. When I got 'home' my little table was already laid for a meal. I could always enjoy their cream, but this time I had my doubts about that queer, grey substance. . . . It must be pudding! Pudding, yes—but fish pudding made with the inevitable jam! I decided to leave that experiment for later. . . .

My wife did not arrive until three o'clock, as she had been watching an operation which lasted for six hours on end. It had been an operation on the brain, for no others are performed in this Stockholm hospital, which is the world centre for that particular branch of surgery. Like a prisoner in the condemned cell at Sing-Sing, I found myself taking an interest in my 'colleague's' fate, though it all seemed rather remote from

me, as my own petition was being heard. When I put
my questions I used medical terms, culled from my
reading. I did not ask her what the cowering, terrified
Being that lurked somewhere behind my tumour was
so plaintively asking me below the threshold of consciousness. I did not ask whether the patient screamed
like a wild beast and struggled to escape when they
split her skull open, whether her blood and brains came
pouring out of the wound or whether at last the victim
fainted on the torture rack, gasping for breath, with
mouth open and staring eyes. Instead, I questioned her
about the operation as if it had been some delicate
experiment in physics or a job of repairs by a watch-
maker.

'Yes, I see! They suspected something wrong in the
frontal lobe. The X-ray of the brain cavities must have
put them on the track. . . . A girl of twenty, you said?
Hm, rather young, isn't she? Did they find it all right?'
'Just fancy, it wasn't there . . . ! Perhaps once in a
thousand cases, the final diagnosis hits on the wrong
spot. Though very rarely, it does sometimes happen
that there are two alternative explanations for the dis-
placement of the filled brain cavities. Can you imagine
—he opened the meninges and there was nothing
there! The whole brain surface was smooth and white.
. . .' 'What on earth did Olivecrona do?' 'Not a muscle
of his face moved. He didn't even bite his lips, though
any surgeon would swear at a moment like that. . . . I
felt so uncomfortable I couldn't look him in the face.
It was like my luck! The very first operation he had

invited me to see, and the world-famous surgeon had gone and made a mistake!' 'So there wasn't a tumour at all?' 'Just you wait! The Professor thought for a second, then quietly sewed up the meninges. He put back the circle of bone he had cut away, and sent the patient to the X-ray room again. He told them there was no need to fill the brain cavities this time. He only wanted one more photograph, and in half an hour he'd go on with the operation. I was horrified. "Professor," I said, "you don't really mean you're going on in half an hour?" He assured me that he was, and that the temple must now be opened. There could be no doubt that the tumour was there. I asked him why he couldn't do it to-morrow, or when this wound had healed. He smiled, "My dear colleague," he said, "once you disturb a brain that has a tumour on it, you must get that tumour out, or else . . . If I don't find the cause of this girl's illness and remove it now, she'll be dead in twenty-four hours." I didn't make any more suggestions. In half an hour's time they brought the patient back and he set to work on the new operation. Round the left temple he cut away a circle of bone as large as the palm of your hand. We all waited, holding our breath. . . . What would he do if he again found nothing? Olivecrona was perfectly calm. You could see that he knew he might make one mistake, but not two. He picked up the meninges, folded it back, and closed each of the veins with a pair of forceps. Then he opened the brain itself and directed his light on to it. We bent over. . . . There, on the smooth, white surface, exactly

in the middle of the opening, was a great, round, red
tumour, like a pomegranate, deeply embedded in the
brain. . . .'

'Well, he got to it after all.'

'That's why it went on so long. The second operation
lasted for four hours till he took the tumour out.'

'And the girl? How's she getting on?'

'She's asleep. The Professor's sure she'll get over it.
And I think so, too, now. . . .'

That afternoon I was to have undergone a fresh
examination, but I asked them to put it off till the next
day. I could not get out of having a bath, and once more
they came to wheel me out in my bed. The bathroom
had a floor of lathes and was none too warm. It contained two deep wooden tubs, like those used in our
vineyards at home. I was handed over to a stout old
woman, and began to wonder nervously if she was going to give me my bath. She supplied the answer by
taking off my dressing-gown, putting me in the tub,
turning on the shower, and starting energetically to
rub me down. I reassured myself by reflecting that I
was in Sweden, where nudity goes for nothing. In the
matter of ablutions women are more expert than we,
and this is a weightier argument than mere conven-
tionality. After a moment I yielded to her scrubbing
with my eyes shut, as if I had been five years old again.
I even enjoyed it when the old thing mumbled and
seemed annoyed as she soaped my hair, probably because I was not holding my poor, splitting head as I

ought to have done. She chattered to me all the time I was in the bath, although she knew perfectly well that I did not understand a syllable.

When I got back to my room they handed me the first letters I had received from Budapest, where it had been known for three days that I should be in Stockholm by now. Dénes gave me a lively account of what was happening. I suspected some hidden meaning between the lines, and when I asked them to read me the parts specially addressed to my wife I triumphantly detected a veiled reference to the fact that legal action was not being taken with regard to my insurance, but that the company was in no mood to be trifled with. In view of the two unpaid premiums they were asking for a new medical examination, but Dénes had the matter in hand and no harm seemed likely to come of it. (As it turned out, harm did come of it, but not to me. A few months later, the insurance company went bankrupt. Perhaps it might have done better to insure itself with me, instead of vice versa.)

At five o'clock the door opened and three people came in—the charming, witty Söjkvist, whom I had met that morning, a young optician, and a tall, broadshouldered, fair-haired man of hundred-per-cent Nordic type.

The Professor. . . .

18

Olivecrona

I recognized him because Söjkvist and the other doctor stood aside respectfully as he came up to my bed, but I knew him in another way, too. I knew who he was almost as soon as they opened the door, although I could not see their faces clearly.

'How d'you do?' he asked, extending his hand. This gave him away. It was not the usual 'Feeling all right?' or 'How are you to-day?' His manner struck me as being on the formal side, but not at all reserved. He had an unforced politeness, which made one feel that he would be just the same at home.

He did not examine me or even ask me any questions. I was not surprised by this, as I knew that his visit was a mere formality. The physicians in charge of my case would be making him a daily report, and he knew all he needed to know about me. I did, however, think it strange that he never even mentioned my illness. A curious notion came into my mind that he had formed some sort of idea about me which had nothing to do with my state of health and which could very well be either right or wrong, but was at all events very positive. I found it a little humiliating that he was not interested in my own views about my condition. He probably regarded me as a layman who had no opinions on such matters, or perhaps, having heard that I was some kind of a poet, he was on his guard against the vagaries of an overheated imagination.

I found this idea wounding to my vanity. While I am a great admirer of science, I claim the respect of its representatives for what I must call—by a much-abused word—my 'artistic' conception of life. Art is a complementary source of truth, for it enlists the help of the imagination to carry mankind beyond a mere observation of facts. Real achievement is possible only when both work in association. This belief made me anxious to confront Olivecrona with a humorous, challenging idea of mine, which I nevertheless put forward in all seriousness. I told him I had a theory that we understand only the composition and physical nature of all the various tumours liable to grow in the human body. Of their role and purpose, or what we might call their intentions, we know even less than we do of our normal organs, though our knowledge of these is imperfect enough. Perhaps this mysterious tumour, despite its apparent work of destruction—and there are also harmless tumours such as the teratomas—wanted to *become* something which would turn out eventually to man's advantage, but for the present wished its purpose to remain unknown. Or it may have set out with the intention of becoming a constructive agent, but had

196

forgotten its original purpose or proved unable to carry it out, perhaps for lack of the necessary means. Or maybe the central government did not *allow* it to achieve its object. Perhaps that government had no programme for the future and drew all its arguments from the past. These tumours might be the first rudimentary attempt, whether conscious or unconscious, at supplying man with some new organ which would direct his evolution on lines as yet unsuspected. Perhaps the human species was endeavouring to grow wings. It might have received a stimulus in that direction from its collective sense of shame at seeing the Individual courageously *make himself* wings when he felt the need to fly, without waiting for Nature to perfect her blind fumblings. Or perhaps, acting on secret orders from the pituitary region, it had devised a plan for a new human sense, which would transmit to the brain centre other messages than those hitherto communicable. Perhaps it was preparing an organic electroscope, an organic antenna (such as insects are provided with) or I know not what device to transmit rays which science, with its inorganic instruments, has not yet been able to detect.

I know for certain that I wanted to put forward some suggestion of this kind to the Professor, but I cannot say how far I succeeded in making myself clear. My hesitating speech, the turmoil inside my head, and my imperfect German were all against me. Olivecrona listened politely for a while, and I felt I had succeeded in arousing his interest as a human being and not as the mere subject of an X-ray report. Soon afterwards, however, he hurried away, saying that it might be an interesting idea to think about if one had plenty of time, but we all had quite enough to do with our everyday jobs—at the factory, the office desk, or the telephone exchange. (I learnt afterwards that he was thinking of himself when he spoke of the telephone operator, as if he were performing the work of an electrician in the brain centre of the body.)

Left to myself again (for Kerstin had gone out with the doctors), I ran over my first impressions of Olivecrona. I cannot say that the man who held my life in his hands had aroused my enthusiasm or inspired me with the blind and reckless confidence I might have expected. I liked him, but he touched no special chord in me. I felt that his outlook both on professional and broader issues was that of a thorough-going materialist. In judging men he would undoubtedly be guided by clear and simple criteria, such as behaviour in life and society. People had already told me in Budapest that he leads a strictly practical life. He spends the hours from seven in the morning till three or later in the afternoon performing cranial operations at the clinic of which he is director. Afterwards, he goes back to his lovely home (for he is a well-to-do man) and his family —he has a wife and three sons. His only amusements are golf and bridge, at which he is an acknowledged expert. He is the author of admirable scientific works, but as yet I knew none of these. He owes his success to an uncanny precision in operating, but, like his master

Cushing, he has also originated new methods and ideas. I noticed one odd peculiarity about him. On a document in the clinic, I happened to observe his signature. I could not read it, but in trying to make out the letters I remarked that his handwriting looked like a woman's. At once I added, 'I should expect it to. Such work needs a woman's touch.'

After thinking things over, I began to ask myself if this Stockholm experiment had really been the only solution open to me. Now that I knew Olivecrona, I had nothing actually against the idea. The Professor seemed to me an admirable specimen of a man, even if he had neither wide cultural interests nor the 'philanthropic' fire of a redeemer burning to save mankind. Although I had not been able to see his face clearly, I felt sure it was an attractive one. He seemed to have a snub nose —a sure sign, they say, of a kindly nature. Moreover, whatever happened, I was not in a position to argue.

On re-reading the above lines I have been struck by the expression, 'who held my life in his hands'. I purposely avoided the more attractive phrase, 'into whose hands I had intrusted my life', for it was not I who proposed that Olivecrona should remove from my brain the tumour I had myself discovered at the clinic in Vienna. The first time I ever heard of his existence was when the Gyulas deduced from various intestinal auguries that I should go to him, in preference to any one else. They seemed to have done the right thing, and in any case it was the doctors' business and not mine.

And yet. . . .

What was that vague, uncertain memory that stirred in me when I tried to recall his face, as I rolled over on to my side and wrapped myself in the yellow blanket? It was as if some detail had been missing from the picture, or as if I myself had forgotten something—something I felt I had known about him before our first meeting. . . .

Yes—what was it? Hadn't we met somewhere before. . . . ? *Where had I seen that man?*

Here I must interrupt my narrative for a moment.

As I write, Little Me has come butting in again, stopping my pen and upsetting my train of thought. He insists that I must break off at once before the 'writer'—that other part of me who produces the imaginative works—tries to go one better than reality. The writer in me sometimes entertains an arrogant belief that he could improve upon the truth by a little deliberate artifice. I have no wish here to discuss the relative value of art and reality, but there is one thing I have learnt since I began to write this account of my illness. Reality as a *genre* requires no helping hand from the artist. This is true both of minor effects such as emphasis and 'limelight' and of literary composition in a wider sense. I cannot explain, but I am obliged to admit, the fact that reality possesses its own technique of composition. It composes as if it intended to say something, grouping and arranging its subject-matter like a professional novelist. I have described elsewhere (and the popular biographies of the day bear me out) that every life-history is at the same time a novel of a life. I now realized that this is true even of technical details such as foreshortening and cross-references. It cost me some sacrifice to act upon my lesson. Several times I had felt tempted to take an incident or reflection out of its proper place and include it with others a few days earlier or later in date which would have caused it to stand out in sharper relief, and thus have thrown a more suggestive light on my story. I came to realize, however, that this was not a wise plan. On arranging my material I saw that it would be a mistake to alter the least link in the chain. Everything would be more comprehensible, and therefore more effective, as it happened in reality, and not as it might have happened. Reality knew, at least symbolically, what material it was arranging, and why.

I was grateful to Little Me for catching the complacent writer in me red-handed. Henceforth, I should continue to dispense with 'literary' artifice, and should let the truth speak for itself, however colourless it might seem. I dare say it would improve the story and make the following pages more effective if I were to write that what turned out to be the symbolical meaning of Olivecrona's appearance in my life was obvious to me from the moment when I lay under the yellow blanket, wondering why I felt that we had met before.

Yes, it would certainly be much better if it had happened like that. But it just didn't. . . .

I am inclined to think that the artistic tastes of reality are to be seen not only in the planning of events with which a narrative deals, but in the period during which one is putting one's memories of them on paper. I am writing this book in serial form, and last Saturday I decided that my meeting with Olivecrona should form the subject of this present chapter. On Sunday I delivered a speech at the Academy of Music in memory of a great Hungarian writer and close friend of mine. At this function I ran into an old acquaintance—a popular actor—whose sense for intricate combinations is so keenly developed that he even plays chess brilliantly. Our conversation turned on my illness, and he asked me about Olivecrona. I started to give him a sketch of the Professor's appearance and personality. After the third sentence, he cut me short.

'But he's the living image of——' and he mentioned a name.

It was not the name of a living or a dead man, but that of a fictitious character, the hero of a play I wrote twenty years ago. The play dealt with a man of great talent and deep feelings, but of an unstable nature, which caused him to be perpetually at war with himself. Being an engineer, he invents an automatic bombing aeroplane to fly without a pilot (of the kind which has since become a reality), but a sceptical friend suggests that he is unconsciously trying to avenge himself on mankind for the fact that his beautiful wife had left him for a gigolo. To prove his disinterested motives the engineer decides to take up the 'plane on its test flight, when the risk of a fatal accident would be considerable. Just as he is wrestling with his fears, the engineer is visited by his *alter ego*, a doctor from the north of Europe, who represents the Solveig motive and who proposes to remove by an operation the brain centre responsible for the fear of death. This he located at the back of the skull in the cerebellum! Having undergone the operation the engineer presents himself to test his aeroplane, and, being no longer afraid of death, he has the courage which enables him to remain alive.

My friend's reason for recalling this play was that he had appeared in it himself. What I told him of Olivecrona reminded him so vividly of his old part as Olson Irjö, the surgeon *alter ego* of the hero, that he told me the expression and gestures I attributed to Olivecrona were precisely the same as those with which he had acted my surgeon on the stage.

19

Pulsating Stars

For several days the weather had been stormy and the window, which had been open, had to be shut again. It was now the beginning of May. This morning the sun shone early into my room—much earlier than it would have done in Hungary at the same time of year. For a moment I saw a golden light on the dome, then it clouded over again. As yet there were hardly any buds on the trees, for they open much later in Sweden. So this was the famous wind from the north! The 'north winds' of our Hungarian weather reports used to conjure up in my mind a vision of wild, Ossianic storms and whirlpools foaming in the fjords. It was nothing like that, yet somehow different from the winds I knew at home. This was a frisky, ethereal, frolicking wind—impetuous, but not ill-tempered. It whistled a devil-may-care tune about the world. The whole universe seemed to be lifted up by it and to be blown clean and pure. My nose, more sensitive now than before my illness, detected a distant aroma of the sea.

It looked as if I were not to be examined to-day.

Pulsating Stars

Although it was already past nine, the attendant had not yet appeared to wheel my bed along the corridor. I snuggled down with my face towards the window. Every now and then I went off to sleep, only to wake up again with a start. Once I caught Kerstin in the act of creeping furtively out of my room. I pretended to see nothing, as I did not feel in a joking mood. Perhaps I was not fully awake, or it may have been my eyes. . . . Yes, I must already be blind! The last vague glimmer I had seen was this morning—a reflection of sunlight on the dome. Since then, everything had been dark. I knew it could not be the clouds that were causing it, for I could hear people walking with a quick, decided step, and a moment ago I caught a click as some one put on the electric light. What worried me was that the whole thing seemed to leave me indifferent. I had to force myself to think about it at all. The question to which I had to try and find an answer was the following: Do you want to face life as a blind man and can you? The mechanical answer was always: I do want to and I can, but I felt no real confidence in it, and soon my self-questioning would begin all over again. Arguments and counter-arguments suggested themselves, none of which carried conviction. I was old enough, I reasoned, to have drawn from the world of light all I should need to sustain me in darkness. What remained for me now was to use the material I had stored up. At last, I could work in peace without being disturbed. Perhaps blindness was not so terrible a condition, after all. . . .

Pulsating Stars

I pictured myself dictating while a faithful secretary took down my words with bated breath. . . . Then, in the evening—but what would that mean to me? How could I distinguish it now? I should know it because in the evening he or she would read aloud, in a gentle, melodious—in a melodious——— Let me see, what was I trying to imagine? Ah, yes! Blindness—that was it. Life as a blind man. . . . I was too tired to go on with the picture. An ironical smile passed over my lips, as I remembered the hero of my play *Butterfly Dance*— Genius, the only man who had eyes amongst the blind. Now, I should have to write its counterpart—the blind man amongst those who could see. With an effort, I tried to remember certain faces. I found I was already beginning to forget them, yet the transition was not a painful one. The rest, too, would be just a transition, a mere difference in degree. I should pass through it as easily as I had come through the stages from perfect sight till now. But what was coming over me. . . . ? A fit of nausea or my heart going wrong this time? That would be something new. . . . The next minute I found myself thinking of a face the details of which I had long since forgotten, but which I had often felt I should one day see again and recognize. Its owner would surely come back into my life. What if, when she did come, she were to find me already . . . ?

That same instant so excruciating a pain shot through me that I reached for the bell.

At lunch time my wife told me she had telephoned

Pulsating Stars

to Oslo. I had a sister married to a Norwegian, who had been living there for twenty-five years and had read somewhere about my illness. She had twice rung up the hospital, where they had given her reassuring news. I was sorry not to have spoken to her. My sister Gizi and I had been on rather curious terms during that quarter of a century. I heard all about her and she all about me, but we never wrote to one another. She had become completely Norwegian, and had two tall, Nordic daughters, pretty girls whose photographs I had seen. My wife's news put me in mind of a naïve reverie I had once indulged in about the episodes of an imaginary journey through Holland, Heligoland, Finland, and Scandinavia. In my day-dream I reached Oslo one winter's afternoon, and, without looking for any one in particular, idled about in a snowy park. I found my way through this city of Ibsen and Knut Hamsun with no other guide than the memories of my youth, when I so longed to travel in the northern countries. I came upon a lake in the woods, now frozen, on which in the summer swans would be floating—the swans of Saint-Saëns. I had built up a whole schoolboy idyll about an accidental encounter with a young girl on her way home from skating, whom I would recognize as my own niece. But I would not let her into the secret at once. To begin with, I should play the foreigner in distress. Then, having asked her the way, I should win her confidence sufficiently to offer her a cup of tea in a quiet *stugan* and amuse her with stories of my childhood, at which she would laugh heartily with her fair

207

head thrown back. I should tell her I was some Bulgarian business man. Eventually, the moment would come when she would get up to go. I should tell her that, as the Bulgarian business man, I had to say an eternal good-bye to her, but as her Hungarian uncle, I insisted on accompanying her home to her mother's....

That afternoon, when they had drawn the heavy curtains, I began to shiver with fever. At last it was clear to me what I had been missing for the past few days. People had noticed my apathetic mood, and now I understood what was causing it. Something had gone from me that afternoon—something I had never missed before since I was capable of thinking at all. At the time I could not have given it a name, but now on looking back, a phrase that suggests itself is, my 'self-dramatizing instinct'. I can find no other expression for the impulse which has kept my life going, though I am especially anxious that Little Me should not misunderstand it, for he makes constant fun of such high-sounding phrases. You know, Little Me, how casual and almost cynical a mask I wear in the ordinary contacts of life. And—just because it is so foreign to your nature —you know how passionate and grandiloquent I am when I talk to myself, and with how studied an art I deliver those silent periods. Yes, I talk to myself theatrically—you needn't be afraid of saying it—using dramatic gestures, as if I were on the stage. It seemed absurd, and yet it was true that my outward carelessness and cynicism, even my cheery, imperturbable manner, have been made possible by these inner theatricals. I have never believed in them, and, in my lucid moments, I am ashamed of the whole thing. Yet without them I should probably have gone under long ago. This secret theatre has made it possible for me to bear with life. It is a stage on which the curtain has never gone up. I have always stood, in buskins and grease paint, looking contemptuously through a hole in the curtain. It amuses me to watch the public, yawning where they cannot see me.

That afternoon I could find my stage no longer. I looked in vain in my heart for the fine words and the taking images. At a moment of depression such as this I had always hoped that the stage would fill with light and colour and music to compensate me for the bright vision I was losing. I had hoped that, after so many years of struggling and suffering, the curtain would go up and that for the first and last time the Public would see the Actor, who had agreed to appear before it on this one occasion in his best declamatory manner, and afterwards vanish for ever down the trap-door. I would have liked futile gipsy music to accompany my bier to the cemetery. After all, I had thirsted in secret for those resounding 'last words' that would be repeated by friends and others unknown to me. . . .

What arrant rubbish! What sentimental trash! In a dim, muddled way, I felt ashamed. I thought of my Oslo idyll and it left me as indifferent as the *Sorrows of Werther* would leave a soldier dying of his wounds.

What could it have been that so depressed me? There

was no sign of the gipsy music. Why, then, could I not hear the colder, purer music of *reality*, until it, too, fell silent for ever? The burden of self-consciousness, which I had lost and gathered up again a thousand times, had slipped off my back. Why, then, was I not happy? Why did I miss so hateful a burden?

And why was it getting so cold here? Didn't they heat the clinic?

It seems that during these hours I was very ill, and not fully conscious. I remember how observation and fancy mingled. I caught myself in the act of seeking desperately amongst the pillows and sheets for a letter I had put in an envelope and hidden in a corner of the bed. It contained some instructions concerning my business and literary affairs, and I wanted to make an alteration in one paragraph. After half an hour's search I realized that not a word of this was true and that the letter had existed only in my imagination, although I had an exact recollection of its phrasing.

I had a similar hallucination about Olivecrona. On one of his afternoon visits we had exchanged a few casual words of no significance. Soon afterwards I imagined that he came in to see me again. This time he seemed quite different from the Olivecrona of a moment ago. His nose had grown longer and he was gesticulating violently. 'Open the window!' he yelled. 'I'm suffocating! The air's fetid in here—open the window!' A week later I still thought this had actually occurred, though it was pure imagination. I remember still another fancy from those days. This time, Olivecrona seemed to be running in the garden at twilight. I saw him rushing about with his red hair loose and his arms waving, while the wind blew his coat against his tall, thin figure. I heard a wild laugh, and wondered if it was he who cried or the storm.

It was late at night when I calmed down again. The window was already pitch black. I did what I could to tranquillize my wife, telling her to go home and leave me to sleep. But sleep would not come. As l turned over in bed and faced the window I tried my hardest to distinguish some sort of shape in the blackness. I fancied that I saw the trees moving just beyond the windowsill. The branches were swaying slowly to right and left in a rhythm as stately as a minuet. Once more, an ironical smile came over my lips in the darkness. Now it was the trees! What a farce that was, too! What a poor, wretched farce! Didn't any one want to understand? Or were people deliberately pretending not to see that all that was just a piece of 'theatre', as well—all that boasted 'life' scattered over the surface of this grave, silent globe as it spins on in darkness? On the skin rash which we called continents something, or rather some one—it was impossible to know who—was trying on costumes and playing innumerable parts to disguise from himself his own uselessness and superfluity. Now he jumped as the grasshopper or the frog, now wriggled as the snake, and now flew with the swift—don't you see how urgent is his errand!—and he was man, too, and the proud oak of the forest, and the shy apple-tree with drooping boughs. Those were not trees dancing a minuet outside my window. They were he, they were myself, acting a part as the swaying trunks and branches waving in the wind. Oh, the shame and the pity of it!

My veins seemed to be convulsively expanding and contracting, and I wanted to feel my pulse. I forgot to do so in the act of staring so fixedly and with so great an effort at the sky that at last I made out a white point in the depths of it. This could only be a star, for the clouds had broken.

A star—a remote white star. Was that what I had been missing, and had its absence kept me from being at peace? A remote white star—could this be the cold music that had come to replace my fevered rhetoric? Had I found that which *was* before I existed, and would *continue to be* after I was gone? Even as a boy of five I loved the star systems of Kepler, Newton, and Laplace more than the fairy tales about heavenly candles and angels' wings. I thought the light years of the Milky Way and the nebulae far more mysterious and splendid than the star-strewn fields of Heaven. A hundred thousand years ago that star shone as it was shining now— the same blazing mass of electrons and protons which no human eye had seen or ever would see. Yet the existence of those minute bodies was more certain than our own, for we were no more than an abnormal association entered into by some of them, upon strictly limited conditions and for a moment of time. It must be that certainty which made the star shine with so calm and white a radiance. And yet—I fancied I saw it twinkling. It twinkled and changed colour. . . .

I remembered that I had lately been reading about the contraction and expansion of certain stars, whose secret was revealed not long ago. The volume of the star's colossal body changes, in some cases every three days and in some every hour. Every three days, every day, or every hour, they contract and expand again to a regular rhythm.

A pulsating star—it must beat like a human heart. . . .

I had drawn myself up in bed to feel my own pulse, when I heard the door open and the electric light go on. A night nurse whom I had not seen before came into the room. I did not inquire why she gave me a double dose of sleeping draught.

'What's the time?' I asked her.

'About quarter past nine. Nine o'clock struck a little while ago.'

She had put something on the table, and lifting my pillow she slipped it underneath and signed to me to lie down again.

'What was that?'

'An air cushion to raise your head. You must get a good sleep to-night. To-morrow morning at half past seven you're going to be operated on.'

20

Avdelning 13

After this announcement I appear to have sunk into a deep sleep, for I can remember nothing more about that evening, nor did I wake up during the night. I slept for ten hours on end and awoke next morning to find that I was being wheeled along the corridor. I was not at all drowsy, in fact my mind was abnormally clear and rational. I had not the slightest sensation of fear or any other emotion. It was the typical early morning mood when one has shaken off the night and its mysteries, and looks at the world with an almost ironical detachment. A day or two ago I had a glimpse from outside of the operating theatre to which I was now being taken. There was so large a No. 13 on the door that, half blind as I was, I could see it distinctly. I lay on my back, looking at the ceiling and waiting in the midst of a whiteness that was almost painful. People were walking close to me. I heard them speaking to one another in low tones, and their whispering struck me as distinctly comical. What could it be they were whispering about, and why had they to be so discreet about it? They had not brought me here to be discreet with me. . . . I could see a white coat approaching, but I watched it only out of the corner of my eye, as I felt no curiosity about the face. They were wheeling me into the theatre now. Four hands laid hold of me by the feet and head and placed me on a narrow table like an ironing-board. They proceeded to turn me over on to my stomach, and fitted my head into an oval hollow, so as to allow of my breathing. I knew that I was to remain for hours in the same attitude, and I tried to find a comfortable position for my face and nose. Before settling down I spied out the land. To right and left of me I could just make out a corner of the sheet. Hardly anything else was visible. I stretched out my arms beside me.

They had begun to whisper once more above my head, but in a more decided tone. This was followed by another silence. I felt a cold touch of metal on the nape of my neck. A muffled whirring sound told me that they were shaving my head. This time the clippers did not stop short at the back, as when the barber uses them to smarten one up behind. They ran the whole length of my skull, removing the hair in long swathes. Afterwards, I felt them soaping my head, but by the time the razor came into play I was already bald.

For some minutes I could hear only the sound of footsteps. Then I felt a slight prick on the top of my head. No doubt they were giving me an injection. I wondered if the Professor had arrived. He probably

215

had, because out of the corner of my eye I now saw two white coats moving. I felt them place some sort of blunt instrument against my head. This looked like the real thing. . . .

There was an infernal scream as the steel plunged into my skull. It sank more and more rapidly through the bone, and the pitch of its scream became louder and more piercing every second. I had just time to say to myself that it must be the electric trephine. They needn't have bothered to be so discreet about their whispering . . . ! My head throbbed and roared like a thousand-horse-power engine suddenly starting up. It thundered as if the infernal regions had opened or the earth were quaking. I never had a chance to think whether it was hurting me or not. Suddenly, there was a violent jerk, and the noise stopped. Having penetrated the skull the point was revolving freely in a space that offered no resistance. I felt a warm, silent rush of liquid inside my head, as if the blood were flowing *inwards* from the hole which had been made.

The silence lasted only a moment. An inch or so further on, the trephine struck into the skull and began again. I observed this second perforation more coldly, for it no longer came as a surprise. Again the trephine shot through the skull, and again the noise stopped. Once more, the blood seemed to rush inwards. Then I had the sensation that they were fumbling about with tubes. I wondered what was happening. Were there to be no more perforations? I heard people hurrying backwards and forwards. The two white coats had disappeared. Suddenly, the operating table began to move.

I was being gently wheeled through open doors and along passages. We went into two lifts, one of which took us up and the other down. I saw the carpet sliding past under my face, and wondered where I was being taken. An iron door closed. The freshness of the air suggested that it must be a large room.

More whispers and footsteps. Some one turned me on to my side and fixed my head. Photographic plates were lowered from the ceiling in front of my face. A violet light shone, followed by darkness and then by the light again. They turned me on to my back and fixed my head in another position. I was in the X-ray room. There were so many curtains, hangings and transverse beams attached to the ceiling that it looked like the back stage of a theatre. Everything was neatly and elegantly lowered from the ceiling as required. On the floor there was no trace of instruments or of the appliances used by this modern Inquisition. I was back once more in the taciturn, smiling Dr. Lysholm's department. The perforations in my skull had therefore been made so that fresh photographs could be taken. They had drained the fluid from my brain cavities, and had filled them with air. That explained all the fumbling I had been conscious of. The actual opening of my skull had still to come. For a long time they kept turning me over, placing me in new positions and photographing me afresh. I began to wonder how long it was all going to last. Occasionally I caught sight of whole figures as they passed, but I saw nothing of Lysholm. One quarter of an hour went by after another.

At last I heard the table creak as they began to wheel me back to the operating theatre. Corridors, lifts, and corridors again. . . . They closed the door of the theatre, and I felt them wheel me under the lamp.

Several minutes passed. No doubt they were examining the photographs. When they came up to me I was lying on my stomach again with my face in the hollow. Some one made my head firm by fixing broad plaster bands over my temples. He pulled them tight and attached them to the edge of the table, so that my head should be perfectly rigid, as if bound to the guillotine. Looking down, I saw a basin under my head, and I could see that as yet there was nothing in it. I felt them tightening the straps by which my hands and feet were to be secured. I tried to move the extremities of my limbs, but they refused to give a millimetre. I could not make the slightest movement of any kind. It was going to be hard work to stand it. I began breathing regularly, to a calm, even rhythm.

There was a fumbling movement about my neck and down my back. This time I knew what was happening, for I had seen it done myself. The nurses were arranging cloths around the area to be operated on. The Professor must be washing his hands, but I could not hear the splashing of water. Perhaps he was talking meanwhile to the other doctors. While I was being photographed he had surely lighted a cigarette in the next room and had laid the stub prudently on the edge of the ash-tray as soon as I was brought back. Afterwards, they would hand him his rubber gloves, put the sterilized gauze over his mouth, and attach the little electric lamp to his forehead.

Dead silence. I felt a succession of little pricks in a circle. Get on—that's enough now! My skin isn't so sensitive as all that. It didn't hurt me, but I distinctly felt the sharp point describe a wide circle on my head. It went over the same path a second time. Then, I felt one long horizontal incision at the back of my neck, though this did not hurt me, either. I heard the tinkle of forceps being jumbled up together and then being handled separately. This went on for a long while. I tried to see what was going on, and managed to make out an area as large as a handkerchief at the bottom of the white coat moving in front of me. It was bespattered with black spots like a speckled handkerchief. Of course, blood spouted from the arteries in jerks, instead of flowing evenly as from the veins. . . . I felt soft gestures, as if my flesh were being opened and folded back. The skull was certainly exposed by now, and the aponeurosis had contracted on to the nape of my neck. For the third time I heard the trephine strike my skull.

'Well, bye-bye, Frici!' I said aloud, and it did not surprise me that no one answered.

Avdelning 13

The noise was now more infernal and continuous than ever. I began to wonder if they couldn't get through the skull, and, in my anxiety, I stiffened my neck, as if I ought to be co-operating with them and holding myself rigid under the impact of the trephine. Otherwise, I felt that the skull might split down the whole of its length. . . . The roar of the trephine completely deafened me. After a while the noise seemed to become a little less strident, as if they were enlarging the aperture already made. At last, it stopped altogether.

Yes, it had actually stopped at last. And high time, too! Don't you think that's enough, Professor? What I mean is. . . . It was more than enough for me, I can tell you! I was in an arrogant, almost bellicose mood and completely conscious. A violent contempt for myself swept over me.

There was a sudden jerk, as if he had seized the opening with a pair of forceps. It was followed by a straining sensation, a feeling of pressure, a cracking sound, and a terrific wrench. . . . Something broke with a dull noise. After a moment it began all over again. A straining sensation, a feeling of pressure, a cracking sound, and a terrific wrench. . . . This process was repeated many times. Each cracking sound reminded me of taking the lid off a jam-jar, while the process as a whole was like splitting open a wooden packing-case, plank by plank. The Professor seemed to be working downwards towards the back of my head, breaking off great pieces of bone as he went. The last one of all seemed so far down my neck that it felt like the topmost vertebra. For a long time it obstinately refused to give way, but at last he managed to wrench it out.

The brutality of the operation had begun to work me up into a frenzy. I abandoned myself to it with a savage voluptuousness, and longed to help him in his task. Gasping for breath, I urged him on with secret exhortations. A veritable fury of destruction seized hold of me. Give it socks! I wanted to shout. Break it up! Smash away! Bust it to bits! Now go for the vertebra! That's it! And again! Catch hold of it harder, man! Twist it round, can't you? You've got to break it! That's the way—it's coming! It's come! Now the next one! Smash into it, butchers! . . . I was struggling for my breath. Everything had gone red in front of my eyes. If I had had an axe or a lump of iron in my hand I should have hit out with it and smashed up myself and every one else, with the wild recklessness of a maniac.

In the midst of my rage I heard a gentle, comforting human voice. Its effect on me was like that of a cool hand on a madman's forehead, or like the calmly lifted sword of a Crusader quelling some African pagan.

'Wie fühlen Sie sich jetzt?'

Could it be Olivecrona's voice? It must have been, although I did not recognize him, for never before or since has it seemed to me so gentle and encouraging— so full of wise sympathy and kindliness. Was *this* his real nature, or was it just because the gauze softened his voice? I felt profoundly ashamed of myself. At the same moment my open head began to hurt. I was surprised to hear my lips form a polite, embarrassed answer, instead of swearing at the pain.

'Danke, Herr Professor, . . . es geht gut!'

After this my mood underwent a change. Once the trephining of the skull was over there ensued a relative silence. But I did not find this silence reassuring. A feeling of weakness came over me, and at the same instant a sudden fear. Good God—I mustn't lose consciousness! What had the Professor said to my wife? 'I don't administer a general anaesthetic to Europeans, for the risk is twenty-five per cent less if a patient remains conscious.' So there *was* something in it after all—we were really co-operating. I had to look after my side of the business, as he was looking after his. It might all depend on thousandths of a millimetre. The moment I lost consciousness I should probably lose my life.

I had to be careful what I was doing. I must concentrate my attention and mechanically produce thoughts which were coherent and sensible. Whatever happened, I had to remain conscious. Let me see, what was the position? I was awake, I knew where I was, and that I was being operated on. At that very moment, in all probability, they were opening the cerebral membrane. That was quite a straightforward job—just a little slit and an application of forceps here and there, like a dressmaker fitting clips on her material. By a logical, yet unexpected process, I thought of Cushing's operation in the amateur film. Yes, that had been a nice, clean piece of work. I remembered saying, 'It looks like the kitchen of a luxury hotel, with the chef in his white coat cleaning a sheep's brains to make croquettes of them.' No, that was an absurd idea. . . . Something better, quickly! What could I think about? Ah yes, that would be an idea. If I could remember where I put my fountain-pen in the drawer of my bed table, I should know I was still conscious. No, that wasn't any good, either. I'd rather try . . . I'd try repeating . . . that Hungarian ballad. Yes, if I tried the ballad, it would help me to measure time as well, for it lasted a quarter of an hour from beginning to end. Anyhow, that would be something gained. I accordingly began: 'The Knight Pázmány strode up and down, In his gloomy castle hall. . . .'

'Wie fühlen Sie sich jetzt?'
'Danke, Herr Professor . . . es geht . . .'

This time it was not my voice at all. I heard someone answer in a high-pitched, quavering tone that came from far away in the distance. What was the use of speaking like that? I'd rather not answer at all. It wasn't worth frightening myself for nothing.

Besides, we ought to be nearing the end now. However long had I been lying strapped on the table? My hands and feet had gone completely numb. Why didn't they loosen the straps a little? Just a shade would be

enough, but that shade would make all the difference.
Did they think I'd throw myself about or upset the
table? It was all a lot of rot! If they didn't undo them
my arms and legs would be bursting soon. They'd die
of suffocation. . . .

Once more there was a sound of pumping and draining, and I could hear the drip, drip of a liquid. How
much longer were these gentlemen going to fumble
about in my skull? They saw how quiet and well-
behaved I was keeping. How long, then, did they pro-
pose to go on with their scratching and manipulating?
Couldn't they do me the honour now and again of telling me what they were doing with my head? After all,
I had been invited to this party, too. . . . I should be
most interested to know how much longer they thought
of using my brain for their soft, woolly fumblings.

Yes, *I* should be interested to know. *I* . . .

The fellow lying here on the table. . . . After all,
those gentlemen and I had never been and would
never again be on such confidential terms with one
another as we were at that moment, for I knew that
they had their fingers in my brain. They had been
draining off some more fluid to get at their objective,
and now they were making my brain ready for the
assault. Yes, it was my brain. I fancied it must be
throbbing now. . . .

Pain? No, I had no pain.

Although my brain didn't hurt at all, it did hurt me

when one of the instruments fell on to the glass slab with a sharp, metallic sound. A certain idea passing through my mind hurt me, too. It had nothing to do with my present situation, but I could not get rid of the idea. It kept forcing itself on my notice, and the attempt to thrust it back was painful.

No, my brain did not hurt. Perhaps it was more exasperating this way than if it had. I would have preferred it to hurt me. More terrifying than any actual pain was the fact that my position seemed *impossible*. It was impossible for a man to be lying here with his skull open and his brain exposed to the outer world—impossible for him to lie here and live. It was impossible, incredible, indecent, for him to remain alive—and not merely alive, but conscious and in his right mind. It wasn't decent or natural—just as it wasn't natural . . . when at an altitude . . . of fifteen thousand feet . . . you had a very heavy object . . . very heavy . . . and it didn't fall . . . as it ought to do. . . . No, not that. . . . What was it, gentlemen, that the duckling said . . . in its quiet, apologetic way . . . when they came . . . to wring its neck . . . ? 'Don't carve me with that knife. . . . It might bring you . . . bad luck. . . !'

Stop that whispering, gentlemen! I could hear everything you say, if I weren't ashamed to listen. . . . They were whispering continually, faster and faster. Faster and faster they kept whispering—and more and more obstinately. They were getting quite shameless about it. Don't whisper like that. . . ! It isn't done, I tell you. It's not my fault. I feel ashamed of the whole thing. Get on, get on, can't you! It's time you covered up my naked brain. . . .

This must have happened at the moment when they removed the band from Olivecrona's forehead, and when, thrusting a micro-lamp into the cavity, he was able to see, and even to touch, the tumour. There it was, growing on the slightly inflamed right side of the cerebellum, under the second lobe of the *pia mater*. It was now eleven o'clock, and the operation had so far been going on for two hours.

21

Addis Ababa

*B*udapest. *Monday*, *May* 4*th*. People were a shade
more glum than usual as they returned to work on
Black Monday. In Budapest—that city of cafés and
newspaper addicts—the chief papers do not appear on
Monday morning. Every one therefore had to be satisfied with the scanty reports which the Monday papers
devoted to the international situation. There were
rumours that Léon Blum was going to form a Government in Paris. The Conservatives muttered that the
week was starting well, as the gipsy said when he was
hanged on a Monday.

Cini, who was now free to do as he liked, was probably enjoying himself. School would be over at twelve,
and his new suit, which my friend B. took him to try
on last Saturday, had just been delivered. His gym
master inquired after me during the first hour, and the
other masters did so later on. In the end it was Cini
who heard from one of them that I was to be operated
on that morning. 'Yes, I remember now. My mother

wrote something about it last week. So it's this morning, is it. . . . ?'

At the house in the Reviczky-ucca Rózsi went fussing about the empty rooms. The weather was so fine now that she could leave the windows open after her dusting. Pali had come home early and was rushing from room to room, with the whole flat to play in. He had unearthed a trumpet from somewhere or other, and was tootling on it to his heart's content, until Rózsi came hurrying in from the kitchen. 'Just you leave that trumpet alone! The very day they're operating on poor master, too! You'd do better to be looking at the Bible and trying to say a prayer for him. . . .' Pali mumbled something to the effect that, if I was so far away, I should never hear the noise he was making. . . . His father, Pál Szabados, had gone out to the Ring, where he had been told he might get a job. As he crossed the Tisza Kálmán-tér he heard some one mention my name, and turned to look in the direction of the voice. Two men were talking outside the theatre.

'Yes, to-day or to-morrow. . . . I read about it. Looks bad, if you ask me.'

'I think so, too. It would be a pity if anything happened to him. . . . He was a decent sort of chap as a man.'

'Did you know him?'

'I once spoke to him for a minute or two. . . .'

Gabi, then staying at Siófok by the Balaton, was on his way down to the lake. He had a little scratch on his hand, and took care to have the local doctor bathe it with iodine as he passed. The doctor asked him if he had any news of me. 'Well, he was very bad the last time I saw him. But he's going to be operated on now. Let me see . . . where did they tell me the place was?' 'Stockholm, wasn't it?' 'Why—how on earth did you know?'

In a shabby little room on the outskirts of Budapest, Mrs. Sch., a kindly old widow lady, who was a great admirer of mine, was sitting as usual at her writing-desk, pen in hand. She was finishing her fourth long letter, but only one of these would reach the post office. She slipped a few rose petals into the envelope. Surely, God would answer her prayers. . . . She would even forgo the pleasure of seeing me again if she could be certain I was going to be cured.

At Gundel's restaurant in the Városliget the tables were already being set out in the garden. The Gellért artificial wave bath was open again, but as yet bathers were not very numerous. The stout, kindly swimming-master was talking to an acquaintance of mine. 'D'you remember how cheery he used to be when he came here last autumn? And that scamp Cini, too? He used to swim under water like an Indian and take off the women's shoes. . . . And how they screamed! He'll be here in the next day or two for sure, you'll see. . . .'

Up on the Svábhegy, in the great, silent hall of the sanatorium, the Senior Physician, Dr. Gy., happened

to be telling some one that I had spent a week on the
first floor of the sanatorium before leaving Hungary,
and that he had seen there was something seriously
wrong.

That morning my name was being mentioned in
many places.

Adolf, the telephonist at my newspaper office, had
already developed a mechanical answer to the reiterated inquiries that came pouring in. 'Yes, he's being
operated on at this moment. We'll be giving a detailed
account in the midday edition of *Az Est*, whether the
operation is over by then or not. . . .' 'I don't quite
follow you—how's that possible?' 'We rang up Stockholm at half-past nine this morning, and we've got
them on the line again now. I hear it's gone very well
so far. . . . Don't mention it! It's a pleasure. . . . Hullo!
Yes, he's just being operated on at this moment. We'll
be giving a detailed account in the midday edition of
Az Est, whether the operation. . . .'

From Stockholm the telephone wire ran on mile
after mile to Budapest, rising and falling over the
Scandinavian mountains, across the pine forests and
beside the blue waters, then on through the keen, salty
air of the sea-shore. It ran between the telegraph posts,
making a bee line for home, as straight as a little pig
squealing and running for its life. The dark green
forest changed to dirty grey waves, and still it ran on
unseeing. Over Hamburg and Nuremberg there were
mountains of piled-up cloud. Still the wire ran on

through Berlin and Vienna, over the valley of the Vág and across the Hungarian plain, where the fields were already green and the fruit-trees showing their leaves. On and on it ran, over the canals of the Budapest suburbs, until at last it reached the centre of the town. Backwards and forwards in a split second it carried the messages of human speech—trivial messages, if the wire that bore them or the posts that bore the wire had been allowed to state their opinion. Those mutilated brothers of the trees had no interest in man's futile communications. 'Do you come from far, brother wire?' whispered a telegraph post at Stockholm. 'What's the news from the south? Is it true that down there the cherry-trees are in blossom? Our trees will have to wait till next month for that, and on me there'll never be flowers again. . . .'

At half-past nine the newspaper rang up my wife. She was summoned away from her anxious vigil in the corridors to give them all the news she could during a fifteen-minute call. A stenographer took down her words verbatim and handed them to the editor, who passed them straight down to the printers, for the newspaper was to be made up at midday. (She gave only facts, without adding any comments of her own, which was the best thing she could have done, both from her point of view as a doctor and from mine.)

'. . . The operation began at nine, and it can hardly end before one o'clock. . . . I listened at the door a moment ago, and I could hear the patient groaning. . . .

231

'. . . The Professor? Oh, he's a most remarkable man. . . .

'. . . Yes, with an electric trephine. . . . They're taking his blood-pressure every minute. . . . They give him oxygen from time to time. . . . If necessary, he'll be given a physiological solution of salt and a blood transfusion. . . . A man of the blood group to which my husband belongs is waiting in the next room to him, but I hope he won't be needed. . . .

'. . . At this moment, they're just removing the bone from the back of the skull. . . .

'. . . He's fully conscious. The Professor is keeping in mental touch with him all the time. It was he who carried out the first perforation of the skull and he took the last X-ray photograph. . . . He's just as good a neurologist as he is a surgeon. . . .

'. . . Oh dear, oh dear! I can see they're just sending for that man . . . ! It may be. . . . Yes, good-bye. . . !'

The newspaper staff were all standing round the telephone. After the stenographer had repeated my message there was a moment's silence, then my colleagues separated again, each one to attend to his own job. Misu hurried along the corridor to supervise the afternoon edition. With luck, he hoped to publish Mussolini's broadcast speech. Pecsus sat down to dictate the sporting column. He could not concentrate properly on it, for he was thinking of the visit he had paid me a fortnight ago. He had entertained me with a description of his journey to Stockholm as a fencing champion, and how he had seen the Prime Minister

skating in the street and making graceful half-turns on
the ice. Little P. was also thinking of me as he wrote
an article in which he was trying to summarize my
work. What was that famous phrase of mine? 'Humour
is no joke to me. . . .' S. remembered a wicked little
caricature I once wrote of him, but afterwards he
remembered one of my poems, and the poet in him
forgave me. The editor was thinking about that doctor
in Budapest. . . . K. sat blinking behind his glasses and
feeling genuinely sad. Then he caught himself writing
a sentence which might come in useful as the beginning of an article on me. 'The little acrobat had reached
the top of the piled-up chairs and was taking out a
violin to play the great melody of his life, when the
whole edifice collapsed under him.' The acrobat was
myself as seen symbolically in one of my early stories.
Alas, in any case, it would have to be written one day.
He need not bother to think of a title. The title would
be my name with a heavy black border. . . .

In the waiting-room of the newspaper an unknown
woman in black was observed to be crying. She spoke
to no one, and the others glanced at her in surprise.
When they asked her whom she wanted to see she did
not answer. . . .

By half-past twelve the paper was on sale. A few
passers-by stopped in the street. When they came to
page 5 they glanced automatically at the clock on the
kiosk. Not over yet! Well, they would read the result
in the evening papers. What else was on? The swimming championship and the match in Vienna and this

business. . . . All on the one afternoon, too! (We are really a sport-loving city.)

The Corso was already gay with life. 'Paper!' One of the passers-by stopped a newspaper seller. 'There's modern journalism for you! He's still on the operating table, and here am I reading about it in Budapest. You don't happen to know what a physiological solution of salt is, do you . . . ?'

White clouds were sailing indifferently above the Citadel, and the great span of the Erzsébet Bridge hung silent and aloof over its river.

In the tram a man was shaking his head. 'I've just been reading this article, and I don't know how any wife can talk so cold-bloodedly while her husband. . . . Now, if it had been *my* wife. . . .'

Some of the photographers put portraits of me in their windows that morning. One firm exhibited a huge photograph in the Vörösmarty-tér. Pista Sz. happened to be passing when they were putting it in the case, and he stood dreaming for a moment in front of my portrait. 'Rather interesting. . . . Must be the last one he had taken. What a queer, humble sort of smile he's got! As if he's asking forgiveness! He must have had the tumour already. There's a look of Buddha about him. . . .'

Miklós's elegant figure came slowly down the Horthy Miklós-út. His asthma was bad again, and he found walking difficult. The novel on Széchenyi he had just published was becoming a best-seller, but it was not of that he was thinking. One of my jokes had come into his mind, and he began to smile. 'If only he gets over this business!' he was thinking. There were one or two things he wanted to say to me, and as soon as I got back he would be able to say them. . . . (My illness was not yet over when he died.)

Dezsö and Zoltán were also thinking of what we should say to one another when we met again. They would have liked to be near me and to cheer me up. 'What are you afraid of, you old donkey? There's nothing in it at all. Let's change the subject, anyway. . . . That sketch you wrote on the death of the dog was a capital piece of work. It's a good thing to make people cry for us occasionally. They appreciate us without any restraint then, because they forget that in reality we're still alive.'

(Neither Dezsö nor Zoltán is alive now.)

V. turned a little pale when he overheard what they were saying about me. 'It's his great day,' he muttered enviously.

People kept stopping my secretary Dénes at every step. What was the latest? Hadn't he heard anything? Sz. was especially faithful and went with him right on to the Margaret Island to make sure of getting all the details. Some one asked Dénes if he didn't happen to have any manuscripts of mine. . . .

At lunch time in my usual café people began to collect for their apéritif. A few friends and acquaintances sat down at my deserted table. Tibor the waiter stood listening to their conversation. They were talking about me, and a keen discussion started on medical matters. 'I tell you frankly, I'm not at all clear as to what a tumour is. Of course, I understand the word. But what does it mean in Frici's case?' 'It isn't a question of Frici's case, you idiot. It's a general term. It means a cyst—cyst or tumour.' 'Then we'll have to call him a tumorist now, instead of a humorist.' 'Not bad! But somebody in Vienna thought of it first. . . .'

A lady guide for foreigners was just calling upon her flock to get out of the charabanc. 'Ladies and gentlemen, this is the Erzsébet Tower. Over there, you see the top of the Jánoshegy, the highest point in Budapest. I would ask you to take particular notice of the view. It's said to be finer than those from the Eiffel Tower and the Campanile. If you don't mind, we'll just go up the Tower for a moment. . . . Ah, so Madam is Swedish? How well you speak German! Yes, I know Sweden a little myself. One of our best friends is there just now— a Hungarian writer. He's undergoing a serious operation. . . . Let me see, what was the surgeon's name? Oli . . . Olive . . . Ah yes! Olivecrona. You may have heard of him perhaps? Really? Is he so famous in Sweden? Then I shan't worry so much.'

At the morgue in the Szvetenay-ucca the corpses were lying peacefully in their zinc cases. The only sound came from the dripping of ice as it melted under

them. Some of them wore an expression of indifference,
and some one of surprise. On every face, there was an
expression of some kind that had no meaning, as it had
no cause. An attendant had sat down on the doorstep to
eat a hunch of bacon. His companion was reading to
him from a newspaper. When he came to the title of
my operation report the attendant cut himself another
slice of bacon.

'Who is he, anyhow?' he asked, in a bored tone.

The big headline of the evening paper was now set
up. It ran: *Italians enter Addis Ababa.*

22

Chrysanthemums

How much longer was it all going on? I understood nothing of these fumblings and creakings, gratings and clicks, and I began to pay no attention to them. I knew that the knives, the forceps, and the scissors were working with magical rapidity, but I was getting impatient of all the endless details. Sometimes, there would be an unexpected silence for several minutes. At such times I became more cheerful, although I realized that it could not yet be the end, for they were all standing motionless round me. Perhaps it was the big turn just beginning, when the music stops and everyone holds his breath. I tried to imagine what was going on. Possibly, having located the tumour, Olivecrona had paused for a moment. He might be concentrating, with wrinkled forehead, to discover the best method of attack. I pictured him weighing one alternative rapidly against another. Could he remove it or was it too deep-seated, after all? He might actually be taking the tumour out, delicately peeling off the surrounding tissue, as one takes the skin from an orange. At that moment a sudden fear possessed me again. Why couldn't I hear a single word now? (A little while ago their whispering had got on my nerves.) Perhaps he had cut the ac . . . acou . . . What was the word? . . . Acoustic nerve. No, that wasn't it. He must be annoyed because I had not answered his questions, and now he wasn't going to ask me any more. I struggled to say something, but I was too exhausted and gave up the attempt. At last, I heard a sound—could it be my voice?—very plaintive and low. Perhaps I was only imagining it. I had to concentrate in order to understand, and the others almost certainly failed to catch it. At first all I heard was a hiss. When I finally understood, I was surprised to hear that the word wasn't at all what I wanted to say.

'Ss . . . straps! Ss . . . straps!' I was whimpering.

The fact that all sensation of pain had disappeared did not encourage me. On the contrary, I found it still more alarming. It was like a silent, ironical menace. I began to look upon it as a preparation for worse to come—an unbearable delay while the instruments of torture were being prepared. It was impossible that they should already be digging about in my brain without hurting me. What could it all mean? The tiniest nerve in that little box which was now broken open had caused me such mad pain a day or so ago that I wanted to smash my skull! After all, one knew how delicate an organ the brain was. You had only to thrust something into it or to strike it hard enough through the skull for your number to be up. . . . Yet all this time . . . they had been poking about in the middle of it . . . with knives and forceps and scissors. . . . How

could a man ever survive such a thing? . . . Perhaps
they ought not to be doing it at all. . . . It might be
better if I told the Professor myself that he'd done
enough. After all, he was no doubt a great surgeon, but
that wasn't saying—. Perhaps he had forgotten . . .
that you only had to thrust something . . . into the
brain . . . if you wanted. . . . Maybe I ought to scream
at once, as if he were hurting me. . . . But he was not
hurting me, so I couldn't very well scream. . . . I made
up my mind to scream at the first sign of pain, but not
because I was getting impatient or frightened. I
shouldn't be sorry if he did hurt me. I'd even be rather
glad—but I should scream just to let them know I was
still alive. It would be a way of reminding them that
they had to be careful what they were doing, and to
hurry up with the whole business. This gentle stirring
and kneading had been going on far too long. Yet they
did seem to be getting quicker and more expert at it
now. Yes, they were very clever. There were not two
ways of looking at it. Oh, very clever—I had to admit
that. . . . How marvellously quick the chef's gestures
were as he stirred and kneaded the ingredients on his
table! I imagined the little heap of flour taking shape
as his fingers went flicking over it. Imperceptibly, he
formed a little hollow and broke an egg with his other
hand. As he poured it in, the yolk shone for a second
under the light, then he went on with his stirring and
kneading. . . . Splendid!

Oh, they could do what they liked, but they mustn't

send me to sleep. . . . That would mean I was done for.

The following pages come before my eyes like a sequence from a film. Try as I may, I cannot say for certain whether I had this experience during the operation itself or during my feverish dreams of the next few days. My excursion in Time (which I shall describe shortly) may have begun at that moment, and is perhaps causing me to place in this chapter a series of pictures which should belong to the next. I can only be sure of one thing. As I sit here, writing this book—half in trance, like a medium taking messages from myself —I am unravelling, with an almost cruel concentration, a film of memory pictures embedded amongst the ganglions and convolutions of my brain. In that film, the following sequence appears *next*, and it is therefore here that I shall include it.

The hallucination consisted in my mind seeming to move freely about the room. There was only a single light, which fell evenly on to the table. Olivecrona (or it might possibly have been myself) seemed to be leaning forward. His coat had caught up on the high stool, and I saw him disengage it with his foot. The lamp on his forehead threw a light into the open cavity of my skull. He had already drained off the yellowish fluid. The lobes of the cerebellum seemed to have subsided and fallen apart of themselves, and I fancied I saw the inside of the opened tumour. He had cauterized the severed veins with a red-hot electric needle. The angi-

Chrysanthemums

oma was already visible, lying within the cyst and a little to one side of it. The tumour itself looked like a great, red globe. In my vision it seemed as large as a small cauliflower. Its surface was embossed so that it formed a kind of pattern, like a cameo with a carved design. The pattern was vaguely suggestive of a female torso. Yes, it was a woman holding a baby to her lips. On the mother's head was a kerchief of Italian lace. The *bambino*, seen in profile, was clinging to his mother's neck. . . .

It seemed almost a pity that Olivecrona was to destroy it. I saw him setting relentlessly to work to singe the edge of the cameo, which was clearly distinguishable from the surrounding brain tissue. The design seemed to become pale and flat, then it faded away altogether as the tumour shrank under the heat. The next step was to remove it, as if with a spoon. I watched him skilfully manipulate a knife that had a little lamp at the end. So light was his touch that it did not at any point penetrate the brain. I saw that Olivecrona was sucking his lower lip. In his schooldays, when he had to draw a geometrical figure or a map in Indian ink or to fill in with green and red the delicate markings of a drawing, he surely used to concentrate precisely in that way, sucking in his lip with satisfaction as he saw that the colour had not run. . . . It was easy going now, as the tumour had come away from its surroundings. To me, it looked like a rubber ball floating in a clear fluid within the larger ball of my skull. Beside it I saw a lump of iron—Heaven knows where it had come from.

Chrysanthemums

Perhaps something had forced its way through the membrane while the carriage was rushing madly along the deserted roads, up hill and down dale, rattling and shaking—or perhaps a piece of shrapnel had fallen there and I hadn't noticed it, because officially the ground wasn't open for firing practice, and, besides, civilians were forbidden to shoot.

No, that wasn't the explanation. . . .

Those magicians with white masks and coats were only extras in a medieval mystery. Olivecrona did not belong to them. Sitting on the high stool in his white surgical coat, he seemed to be leaning forward, as if to manipulate the pegs and controls of a telephone exchange on the switchboard of my open brain. He was continually clearing and connecting the lines. I could see that he knew his way perfectly through that Gordian knot of delicate wires. He knew who wanted to talk and to whom, and he sat quietly looking on while the conflicting messages grew ever more disturbing and confused. He paid no more attention to their growing excitement than was necessary to supervise the communications, for he felt no personal curiosity as to their nature. It was wise of him to sit there aloof from it all. The messages were becoming ever more clamorous and insistent. What arguments, what battles, what demands, entreaties, and threats came flashing over the wires! Every voice claimed priority, and to each its own particular worry seemed the most urgent of all. What a racket, what a hullaballoo! All at once, from

Chrysanthemums

far away, a foreign country put through a request for a line. In a superior tone it called for the superintendent, passing over the heads of the lesser employees. It appeared so self-possessed that one felt the greatest calm must obtain in its own country. Was it my instinct of self-preservation calling from some remoter cavity of the brain? Faint, secondary noises began to buzz and growl. Olivecrona set calmly clearing and connecting the lines, but the foreign voice refused to give way. It became ever more insistent and provoking. 'What's that? Didn't you hear what I said? Answer me at once! I want a definite "yes" or "no".' Then came an appeasing voice from the exchange. 'Just a moment, please! I've another urgent call on. . . .' 'Put me through at once! My business is far more important than your petty local calls. I mean to have my answer. . . ! I don't care about anything else. Yes or no? Answer me or I'll——' 'I'm very sorry, I can't say for the present. I've other things to attend to. . . .' 'Let me finish my sentence, will you? Hullo, hullo, hullo. . . !'

The voice from the foreign exchange rose to an agonized shriek. From the other lines came a scandalized titter of amusement. 'Just listen to that! Ssh. . . . Isn't it shocking the way they talk. . . !' But Olivecrona was neither amused nor perturbed. With his eyes fixed on the switchboard he saw that the shouting voice had been too much for the frail wire and the current far too strong. The wire began to glow with a faint ominous red, and in a second the fine grey envelope about it flared up. *A fuse* . . .! With a swift gesture

244

he manipulated the controls and cut the current. There was a deathly silence, as if the main current of all had been cut off. . . . In the midst of it his magician's fingers went rapidly to work. He touched the wire, over which a crust had formed as a result of the burn, and with his sharp knife cautiously scraped the latter off, till he could remove it.

I was struggling convulsively to cling on with my short, clumsy fingers. He gently pushed them aside. 'Careful! You mustn't touch it now!' 'Yes, Professor, I understand. . . . But if I don't hang on, I shall slip down that dark precipice. My feet have nowhere to hold.' 'Try and be patient! You've got to hang on a bit longer.' 'Yes, Professor. . . . It's hard, though—very hard.' 'You ought to keep quiet—that's the way to bear it. You ought to have kept quiet all your life. . . .' 'What d'you mean?' He leant over my ear. His voice was a mere whisper, so that only we two should hear. 'You saw that business with the fused wire, didn't you? Well, that happened just because you insisted on shouting, because you would keep on protesting all your life and working yourself up. Didn't you always feel when you were doing it that your head seemed ready to burst? The rush of blood makes all those delicate veins in it swell up. Round one of them little congeries of blood vessels began to form. And that was how the whole business of your tumour started. . . .' 'Yes, I see what you mean—I think I understand. . . . But understand *me*, Professor! How could I put up . . . with all the injustice . . . and all the cruelty . . . and the greedy, selfish passions? . . . When I was only a child . . . they used to punish me . . . though I was perfectly innocent. . . . Nobody listened to my defence. . . . They just slammed the door in my face. . . . My answer was to kick it . . . and hammer on it with my fists. . . . There are things you can't put up with. . . .' 'Oh yes, you can! And, what's more, you must. . . .' 'I understand . . . I see what you're driving at now . . . I've got to keep quiet . . . got to take it gently. You want me to relax . . . well, look at me now—isn't that better?' 'Wie fühlen Sie sich jetzt?' 'Danke, danke, danke, Herr Professor. . . .'

I knew for certain that I had heard the same question three times. From that moment my fear vanished, and with the fear went my desire to resist. It is very hard for me now to say whether I was still conscious at that moment, but I think it most probable that I was no longer afraid of losing consciousness. In any case, I ceased to feel any anxiety as to how much longer the operation was going on. A vague feeling of indifference came over me. Perhaps I even felt something a shade more agreeable than mere indifference. It would be too much to say that I enjoyed my situation, but I had grown, as it were, accustomed to it. I settled down quietly, and gave up all attempt at resistance.

My last memory is of a slight surprise, followed by a

fresh wave of panic. A feeling had come over me that I had nothing in particular to worry about. I only wanted to observe what was going on round about me. This I proceeded to do, but after a minute or so I found myself engaged in a private argument. They couldn't possibly be flowers! But they obviously were! How in Heaven's name *could* they be flowers? I had no idea about that, but flowers they undoubtedly were. Two big white chrysanthemums standing just in front of my nose, as plain as a pikestaff! They were not cotton wool. They were not gauze, either. I looked at them out of the corner of my eye, just as a moment ago I had been looking at the doctor's white coat. Only the flower heads were visible, like two enormous feather brooms. Rather a queer sight in a Scandinavian operating theatre. . . . I decided that there was only one thing to be done. I must keep calm and everything would explain itself. Of course, I knew what they were for—they were testing my reflexes again! It was like the blood test and the questions. They wanted to find out if I still had any sense of smell. That was why they had put them right in front of my nose. But chrysanthemums hadn't much scent. . . . What if——? A sudden panic laid hold of me . . . I must be lying on my bier!

Then, in a flash I understood. It was like the moment when one has dreamt of being upside down and on waking finds the bed in its normal position, or perhaps like the sensation experienced by a beetle that has been lying on its back and has at last succeeded in turning over. I realized that it was the ceiling I was looking at, and not the floor. . . .

I was lying on my back in my own room, with the two chrysanthemums in a slender vase on my bed table. I felt it must be about five o'clock. During the last hour of the operation I had been unconscious, and, when they undid the straps, my hands and feet fell limply away under their fingers.

23

An Experiment with Time

In describing the first few days after my operation I am obliged to eke out my memories with details supplied by other people. I regret this, but I cannot help it, for my perception of space and time was now thrown completely out of gear.

I was afterwards told by a number of people that on coming round I showed signs of being dangerously restive. I first turned over on my back. Then, because of the unaccustomed position of my head, I suddenly wanted to sit up. Perhaps I took the huge turban of bandages for an uncomfortably high pillow. In any case, I wanted my nurses to take it away.

The consequence was that they rushed at me in alarm to make me lie down again. This had the effect of annoying me, and I put up an indignant resistance. I was apparently offended by the idea that they ventured to doubt my wisdom. My first impulse was to explain to them (for I was convinced that I was talking rationally) that not only would it do me no harm, but that from the static point of view it was the best thing possible, as it would keep the various communicating tubes of the body in equilibrium. Seeing that they did not yield to this argument, I claimed to know better than any one else what was good for me. I could see that there were only women in the room, one of these being my wife. This encouraged me to launch out into an analysis of the character of women in general, my object being to prove the inferiority of the feminine mind. I did not mince my words, as I was in a rather excited mood and women couldn't be expected to understand such matters, anyhow. They invariably confused theory and practice, and were incapable of realizing that ninety per cent of science was mere theory. We had only to let ourselves be governed by reason, continually adapting ourselves to circumstances, and drawing fresh conclusions from the facts. My wife kept anxiously pushing me back into the bed, and informed me that Fröken Kerstin had instructions to keep me there. It was this remark which finally lost her the argument, as I could have put up with anything at a pinch, but not with a reference to the authorities. I thereupon declared that women were all pretentious idiots with no understanding of life. They gave themselves airs by imitating from men phrases which they used as the current coin of their conversation. They wanted to have their finger in everything, and they always knew better than any one else. As for Kerstin, there was something I had preferred not to let her know as yet, but it was high time she heard it now. She was every bit as silly a goose as the others, and I behaved politely to her and trusted her not because I thought her intelligent, but because she had a kindly disposition. She's a stupid goose, I insisted, and I did not hesitate to say it in several languages, so that there should be no risk of her failing to understand, if she happened to be in the room. '*Eine dumme Gans*, a silly goose, *une oie stupide.* . . .'

Interpreting the momentary surprise of the others as a sign of my triumph, I wanted to exploit it immediately and take over supreme command. I sat bolt upright, and began to order them about with imprecations and threats. I noticed that what alarmed them most was to see me move my head, so I threw this weapon into the balance like Varus's sword. At the least sign of resistance or contradiction I began to shake the huge diver's helmet of bandages. I might have been a real diver standing up to his neck in the sea and threatening to vanish once and for all with the treasure, unless his terms were accepted.

Without properly understanding the position, I somehow realized that these terms were hardly in proportion to my high-sounding arguments. My wife assures me that I began by asking, with the utmost insistence, for a glass of apricot brandy. When this had been promised me I became more exacting and declared that I intended to play tennis—a surprising decision in view of the fact that I have never played nor felt like playing tennis in my life. Possibly, however, this was no more than an unconscious expression of gratitude towards the King of Sweden, of whom I had heard a few days before that, despite his age, he had won a prize at an international championship.

After this display, and perhaps with the idea of punishing me for my having been insufficiently objective, they must have given me a sleeping draught, for my bellicose instincts were appeased. When I came round again I was pleased to see that it was light, and I began to devise a system for counting time. As a basis I apparently chose the impressionistic method usual amongst primitive peoples. I went entirely by the alternation of light and darkness. This led afterwards to great confusion, and was the source of bitter arguments. I have formed the habit of relying upon myself, but, as the calendar had long ceased to interest me, I now realized for the first time that my self-confidence had been exaggerated. I was pleased to see the daylight, and it never occurred to me to doubt that this could be anything but the following day. I was convinced that it was the morning, and not the afternoon. My feeling was that I had slept throughout the first night, and that now I had only to wait for the next. I did not notice the absence of lunch and dinner, for I had no appetite. Presumably the doctors knew this and were wisely not troubling me to eat meals, or be washed or turned over in bed. The attendants crept in and out of my room on tiptoe. Hardly any one spoke to me, and when they did so I told them roughly to leave me alone, for I had enough to think about as it was. I suspect now that I was thinking only about the best methods of measuring time, for my position was like that of a captive or a sleeper whose subconscious mind clings to the idea that he must get up at half-past seven. I saw nothing unusual in the approach of darkness when I began to feel sleepy again. I thought it must be because I was tired that I could remember practically nothing of that day, and I bade it farewell with a sense of relief when it seemed once more to change into night. Several times I heard the deep, resounding chimes of the clock-tower, but I did not count the strokes, nor did I notice that the clock always struck many times, and never once or twice only. I caught sight of Olivecrona and recognized him from his height. He was standing in the doorway in a white coat, and did not come nearer. I saw him nod with an encouraging, satisfied look.

Twelve times it darkened, and twelve times the light returned. I counted the changes proudly, with a view to making more complicated calculations. The fact that these periods of time were all equal in length did not arouse my suspicions. I saw nothing to be surprised at in the fact that it was always the same people who came round me, that they always asked me the same questions, to which I always mumbled the same replies, or that my mood never seemed to undergo any essential change. It did not strike me as curious that Olivecrona appeared five or six times in the doorway, exactly as before, wearing the same white coat, or that he never came any nearer to me, but invariably disappeared with the same encouraging, satisfied nod.

An Experiment with Time

All this was a curious, reversed example of the *déjà vu* or what Bergson calls the 'memory of the present'. Instead of blending two or more images (memories and impressions) into one, I had divided a single impression into twelve separate images, carefully adding up all my sleeping and waking periods.

When I woke up for the last time it was really dark. My wife was writing at the table by the window.

'When are they going to take off my bandages?' I asked her suddenly, though without any intention of starting an argument.

'Hullo, are you awake? It isn't hurting you, is it?'

'No, I've no pain—but when are they going to take off my bandages?'

She began to laugh.

'You're in a bit of a hurry, aren't you? They'll take them off all in good time. . . . If you mean when are they going to change them, they aren't. When the bandages come off, it'll be for good.'

'Then they won't do it till to-morrow?'

I heard her laugh again.

'To-morrow—good Heavens no! In a week or ten days, perhaps!'

I was beginning to get annoyed.

'D'you mean to say they're going to leave all this on my head for three weeks? That's a bit too much. . . . Are you sure you haven't made a mistake?'

'Three weeks? Who said anything about three weeks?'

'You told me they'd be off in a week or ten days.'

An Experiment with Time

'Well——?'

'Twelve days added to that makes three weeks.'

'How d'you mean—twelve days?'

'I don't know what you're talking about. ... Wasn't I operated on twelve days ago?'

This time her laugh had a note of anxiety in it.

'Look here—you'd better stop talking rubbish.'

'Well, when *was* the operation?'

'This morning.'

I said nothing, but turned over in bed with my back to her. I felt a bitter grievance against the world. What riled me most was the insolence of the medical profession in thus assuming the right to deceive a patient into thinking that he had over-estimated the passage of time, so as to make him more docile during the days to come. Did they think I was going to swallow anything now, just because my brain had been operated on? ... When they came to ask me some more questions I pretended I was asleep.

My wife tried to entertain me by describing how a big Swedish newspaper had published a long interview we gave to a lady journalist. There was even a photograph of us both. A special article had appeared about her, in which she was praised as a doctor and as an 'interesting personality'. I obstinately refused to answer. What interested her in the whole story was the part that concerned herself, but then I never had any illusions on that score. ... I was only a poor, feeble-minded patient to whom it was of no consequence whether he learnt the truth or not. And what use was the truth, anyhow, if it did not serve our vital interests? Women had never cared about the truth, but only about their truth. For a moment I caught a glimpse of the sad face of Strindberg, with his wild hair in disorder. Yes, things were still exactly the same as the master of my youth had depicted them. It was not a mere accident that I had come to his country on pilgrimage to show him my open head, as I had seen his long ago in his books.

I pretended to be asleep, and waited impatiently for my wife to go out. No sooner had she done so than I turned over on to my back and rang the bell. It was Kerstin herself who answered.

'You mustn't tire yourself, you know!'

'Don't worry about that! Please shut the door, Fröken Kerstin, and come here for a moment. I want you to tell me—without any subterfuge—when they did my operation.'

'You mean what time it began? At eight o'clock.'

'I know that, but eight o'clock when?'

'Why, this morning!'

'I see. . . . Thank you. Then, in your opinion, what day of the week is it now?'

'Monday.'

'I see. . . . Well, that'll be all, thank you. I don't want anything more.'

'Let me just arrange your pillow.'

'No, it's all right. Leave it alone.'

'Now, just you let me tidy it up. . . .'

Kerstin claims that I allowed her to arrange my pillow for a moment without making any complaint, but that when she gently put my head aside I pulled my arm like lightning from under the bedspread and struck her hand as savagely as a beast of prey. Thinking she must have hurt me, she excused herself and went out. I do not remember this incident, but I am sure she never hurt me. I lay in bed, afterwards, gasping for breath and swearing.

So they had done me all right! When counting the days I had forgotten that other people were also free to reckon time as they pleased, and that they didn't care tuppence about all the fuss I was making to register events by my own system. For some reason, no doubt on preposterous medical grounds, they were anxious to deceive me, and now the whole gang were in agreement. I was helpless in their hands, and if they wanted they could upset the whole Gregorian calendar without my being able to move a finger. All the confidence and hope I had built up during those twelve days were blown to the winds. I felt as if I had been flung out of a bright tavern after being beaten by the gay revellers who were now making fun of my sufferings from the window. To-day was yesterday and yesterday would be to-morrow. . . .

When Olivecrona came to see me, I received him more diplomatically, and did not ask him a direct question.

'Thank you, Professor—I feel all right. Oh, would you mind, Professor—can you just spare me a moment?

Yes, excuse me for troubling you. . . . I don't know if I'm expressing myself clearly. . . . You are certainly familiar with the theories of Kant regarding our perception of space and time. . . . I don't know them very well myself. . . . But I should just like to add. . . . I mean, do you, as a doctor, think it possible, Professor—listen carefully, please—that our perception of time . . . is something . . . that exists independently . . . of the fact of our attitude . . . or *a posteriori.* . . .'

The Professor touched my hand.

'I see you're quite your old self again.'

And with that he hurried away.

24

Half a Dog running to Trelleborg

After this incident two real days went by which I scarcely remember at all. I have a few notes made by my wife—a page or two altogether—in which she took down some of my disjointed remarks. They are not worth quoting here, as they read like an account of the ravings in a madhouse—pseudo-profound remarks, displays of 'learning', and pedantic statements about matters of no interest. These notes make me think of an inventory prepared by some one after his house has been burgled. It looks as if I had anxiously turned over every image that rose up in my mind or came to me from outside, so as to make sure whether it had kept all the associations which it should possess for a normal mind. Wasn't there anything missing from my favourite china service. . . ? While I anxiously rummaged through the contents of my burgled brain I chattered to myself in a desultory fashion. 'There's that important letter I must send. . . . A stamp in the corner, because of the authorities. . . . Kerstin'll have to post it. . . . Women's sense of logic isn't reliable. . . . But perhaps

259

they can be trusted to do that. . . . As what-d'you-call-him said . . . that French fellow . . . ! I'll remember his name in a moment. . . .' Similarly, I have noticed that when people come round after a fainting fit, they are apt to worry about trifles, such as whether they have lost their handkerchief. One never hears anything of those grandiose visions from the threshold of life and death which the unobservant and the romantically minded so fondly picture. My ravings also included a good many jokes, paradoxes, and *bons mots*—they wouldn't have been my ravings without them. While I remember hardly anything of the first two days, I have an extremely vivid recollection of the three that followed, although I did not keep count of them and was conscious only for short intervals. Arachnitis or inflammation of the cerebral membrane had set in, accompanied by a temperature of 104, as I was told when out of danger.

There was no mirror on the wall, yet I seemed all the time to be watching a reflection of myself and to remain constantly in the same position.

Yes, I seemed to be in the same position all the time. . . . I lay on my right side, with my back to the window, looking fixedly at the door handle. I was bent double as if I had stomach ache, with my head resting sideways on the sheet and not on the pillow, which I had pushed away. I kept my head as near as possible to the edge, so that it was almost hanging over the side of the bed.

Half a Dog running to Trelleborg

In this attitude I lay hour after hour, absorbed by my own thoughts. I was not feeling at all sorry for myself, and I did not ask for anybody or anything, yet I seemed to be lying in wait with my nerves on edge. When any one came into the room I did not move but remained in the same position, staring at the floor, as if their presence did not interest me. Then, just as they were on the point of going out, I would begin to speak in a monotonous, slightly sing-song voice. It was always the same statement I made, ending with a dry, matter-of-fact question. I remember every word, and even the moment when I composed the sentences with a view to their being clearly understood. 'I want to speak to you for a minute. Please listen to me carefully. I know that complications have set in. I am an adult, and I have the right to know what has happened. I have also a family, and I wish to make certain arrangements. Will you kindly tell me exactly how many more days I can expect to live?'

The answers I received were always meaningless, but I continued perseveringly to repeat my phrases like a well-learnt lesson, hurrying to get them out before each visitor left the room. When they had gone I would say the question over again to myself, then I would be quiet once more. My head felt as heavy as a great ball of lead, and was listless and hot. I tried to balance it delicately on the edge of the bed, for I felt that if I were to lean forward a little more it would fall on to the floor with a crash. My skull seemed to have mingled with the surrounding bandages, as if both formed only one

261

body. This explained why it seemed so enormous—for my body by comparison was thin and wretched. I felt I had withered away to nothing.

These, however, were only spasmodic moods that coincided with my rare intervals of consciousness. The rest was like a long dream in which everything was obscurely jumbled up, for it began again at the same point each time I lost consciousness.

All these external factors—the bed, my head lying on the edge of it, the door and my reiterated request—formed, as it were, a series of islands rising out of a black and rumbling sea. That sea was empty. It had depth, but no surface, no limits and no shores. . . .

Somewhere in the depths of this shoreless Limbo I was running. Yet, though I ran breathlessly and without stopping, I remained always in the same place, at an equal distance from my goal and my starting-point. I made no progress, yet I could not remain behind. Lifting my head in the air, I howled at the torture of my impossible position.

I was a big, black dog, a cross, it appeared, between a retriever and a Great Dane, but only one side of me was complete. That was why I was galloping through the night towards Trelleborg. At Trelleborg the train had cut me in half from head to tail, and the remaining portion of me was galloping with a feverish eagerness along the railway line, so that I could find my lost half at Trelleborg before it was too late, and while a spark of life still remained in it. As I ran I was making cold, yet desperate calculations. I knew that the train journey here had lasted exactly nine and a half hours. A dog might perhaps run the same distance in fifteen hours. Of course, I had to take into consideration the fact that I was running on two legs only—the front and back legs of my left side. This, however, had the advantage of giving me only half the weight to carry. One blessing was that, my only eye being on the left, I could not see the horrible, lacerated surface of my other side, which would have caused me to faint and have stopped me from running on.

I could have run on steadily, with my half head hanging calmly down and without even howling, if only the scenery were not running too. I was frightened by the way it streamed past in the opposite direction, as if I had been watching it from a railway train. I had never expected to make this alarming discovery when running on foot. The night persisted wickedly in running, too, and I could not do otherwise than run still *faster*, if I were to get there first. Sometimes I seemed to be succeeding, sometimes the reverse, and when this happened, I howled and moaned with fear.

It was a fine, cold night. I had crossed the country on my way to Stockholm and could find my bearings, if I lost sight of the rails for a moment, but I did my best to remain near them. I ran beside and sometimes actually between them, though I would leap to one side when I thought I heard the approaching rumble of a train: *the rumble of an invisible train.* This rumble usually stopped, and I would jump back between the rails and run on as before. I knew it had been mere imagination, like that other idea of the dog struggling behind me in the twilight between Szentendre and the island. . . .

I was very cold. There was a cloudless sky, and I knew that close behind me the moon was shining. When I raised my head to howl, I wanted to look for it in the sky. I could almost see it, but I felt it was hurting my neck to turn round. All the fields were bathed in its mysterious light. The whole countryside lay open under the moon—the infinite pine forests, the hills, the valleys, the red houses, and, here and there amongst the trees, a shimmer of blue waters. I longed to rest, but this was out of the question. Whatever happened, I had to get to Trelleborg before it was too late and while the moonlight still lasted. I felt I must hurry, because the moon might go down before long, and the whole countryside be plunged in darkness. If it did so, I should lose sight of my only guiding line—the rails. I desperately needed that faint light, which was just sufficient for me. Sometimes I took alarm at the thought that perhaps it was not the moon after all. This pale, uncertain glow might be all I could see of the sunlight. . . . My fears on that score gave me yet another reason for running faster. Now and again I heard something wailing and sighing, and at such moments I always shivered with the cold. It was the howling of the Daughter of the Wind, of whom I had read in a forgotten fairy tale of my childhood. At six years of age I had longed so eagerly to meet her that I used to wander

264

off alone into the forest on the witches' island at Pecel. I never succeeded in finding her, and here she was wailing and laughing at me, yet I could not see her even now. I could not play with her the sweet and terrible game I had devised as a child, and of which I alone had the secret.

Another island rose out of the depths. The door opened and I bent forward, blinking uncertainly. A doctor entered the room. He was not Olivecrona, but I had seen him before, though I did not know his name. He leant over me and took my temperature. Afterwards I heard him whispering to somebody. As he was going out I mechanically began to repeat my message.

'I am an adult. I know that complications have set in. I have the right to know what has happened. . . .' In a moment, however, I was running on again between the curving railway lines towards Trelleborg.

Another island. This time it was more than an island —a veritable oasis. It must have occurred towards the end of my long nightmare. The door and the handle opposite me had never moved, and the room was empty. Yet I was not alone. Some one was playing the piano far away. I did not know there was such a thing in the hospital, but perhaps it had been put there for the benefit of the patients, as music may have proved beneficial to those with trephined skulls. . . . The melody was borne very softly in to me, and I could hear only the vibrations of the wires. The striking of the keys did not reach so far. With a feeling of incredulity I noticed that all my resentment and depression seemed to have vanished. My head was clear and light once more, and I felt an intense weariness such as only the mind can know when its task is over. The soft, appeasing music touched my ear like cool water on the lips of some pilgrim thirsting in the Sahara.

Für Elise—that delicious trifle of Beethoven's, which the ageing giant wrote for a little girl of ten. One could actually feel the old bear capering through his pure and innocent little dance before the dawn of beauty. I drank in the music like a new-born babe taking his first breath of air, intoxicated and a little ashamed by such an excess of joy. Was it possible, I whispered—was it possible that I was still alive? Beethoven was dead, but I was to go on living. . . . Slowly the tears began to run down my throat and on to the sheet in front of me.

Later on, my wife and Olivecrona came in. He made me sit up in bed, and examined me for a long while. I said nothing this time, but I noticed that his manner became brisker.

'Tell me,' he asked, as he got up, 'how long has this gone on?'

My wife explained something to him.

'In that case,' said the Professor, 'we'll put an end to it now. That'll have been just enough. I'll come back in a moment.'

He left the room. My wife began to assure me there was nothing I need be afraid of. I had no idea what she was talking about, and in any case I wasn't interested. In a minute or two Olivecrona returned with a huge needle protruding from a syringe.

'I'm going to drain off a little fluid,' he explained. 'Just lean forward, will you? As far as you can.'

I obeyed.

'Now we're going to see a masterpiece,' remarked my wife in a flattering tone. This was no doubt her way of expressing her gratitude to the Professor for choosing to carry out so simple an operation himself. She meant well, but she would have done better to say nothing. Possibly her remark distracted Olivecrona's attention for an instant. In any case, it was an unlucky minute for all three of us. The next second I let out a yell like a jackal. The needle had probably entered a ganglion, and it may well have been the first time in his life that such a thing had happened to Olivecrona. The pain lasted only for a moment or two, but never have I experienced anything so agonizing. During the whole of my illness this was the only time I cried out in pain.

I recovered my objectivity at once, and asked him how much fluid he had drawn off through the spinal canal. 'Half a teacupful,' he answered, in the same even tone. 'But there will be more to come. . . .'

After this little operation I again went off to sleep and it was now that I dreamt the last chapter of my nightmare. During the time I had been awake the bisected dog had apparently reached Trelleborg. Day was breaking and the low wooden houses, the station buildings, and the docks were clearly visible. I came upon a trace of blood and dragged myself along it, following the scent, till I found myself by the sea-shore. The trail led down towards the water, and I stepped in cautiously. My other half was lying on a little sand-bank, where the gentle waves had carried it. It was already beginning to decay. I licked it with some embarrassment and attempted to drag it out. But even as I did so, I felt that this was a mere act of piety, for I was whole again and needed it no longer.

Late that afternoon I demanded the right to sit up in bed. 'It can't be done,' they told me. However, I could lie on my back and they would prop my head up.

'99.6!' said Kerstin proudly, when she had taken my temperature.

I behaved as if it were the most natural thing in the world, though I couldn't help saying, 'Not bad—twenty-four hours after the operation.'

This time there was a happy laugh.

'Twenty-four hours, you say! It'll be a week to-morrow since you were operated on.'

25

'Let his Bonds be Loosened'

Once more I could recognize and check the days, each one with its twenty-four hours and a name and number of its own. They succeeded one another again without interruption, as they had been doing since creation began, or at least since those thrilling days after the Flood when the rainbow bore its giant notice: 'While the earth remaineth, seedtime and harvest, and cold and heat, and summer and winter, and day and night shall not cease.' And so to this day cold and heat, suffering and joy, fear and hope, faith and despair, come as one another's shadow in the experience of man.

Each day now brought forth its torture, and each its own peculiar joy. I remember one morning which began with the magnificent realization that *food had a taste again*—the old, familiar, delicious tastes and some that were entirely new! The Swedish cheese made with carraway seeds, which I had never eaten before, proved to be excellent, and so did the salmon with jam and the other specialities of the *smörgåsbord*. What an intoxication and joy they were to me—those rediscovered flavours of the tongue and palate!

But misery was not far behind. A few hours later I was turning over various plans for suicide as a result of my shame when the enema which had been administered to me under such humiliating circumstances failed to produce any effect. That day I had my first experience of a catheter, and I felt as ashamed of myself as a dog with a tin on its tail. What bothered me most was the imperturbable way in which the nurses went about their business. I could not reconcile myself to the sight of all those fair heads and milk-white skins which seemed incapable of blushing.

After a while I made my peace with the world, and by the time Olivecrona appeared in my room I was only anxious to find some beautiful way of expressing the gratitude I felt to him. That day, however, he was gruff and short of speech. He seemed impatient to get away, and was apparently thinking of other things. I even felt a touch of impatience in the words, flattering though they were, with which he took leave of me at the door.

'Who are you in your own country?' he asked me in a suspicious tone. 'I'm being inundated with letters from people in Hungary congratulating me on saving your life.'

As soon as he had gone I looked straight in front of me with a smile, and recited Heine's poem in a low voice as a message to Olivecrona in the corridor.

' Let his Bonds be Loosened '

Ich bin ein . . . Dichter
Bekannt in . . . Land,
Nennt man die besten Namen,
So wird auch der meine genannt. . . .

That afternoon I understood why Olivecrona had seemed to be preoccupied.

At four o'clock, when my visitors—a number of Hungarians living in Stockholm, and the charming Hungarian Minister, Leffler, the adventurous Captain Grundböck and Consul Trulson—left me, my wife remained in the room. I could see that she was worried. She got up, went out, came back restlessly and paid no attention to what I said.

'Is there something wrong?' I asked, after a lengthy silence.

She struggled for a moment to put me off, then burst out.

'The Viking' (our nickname for Olivecrona) 'has been bothering me to tell you something. He's asked me three times.'

Another pause.

'Well——?'

'After all, I don't see why there's such a hurry about it. They may still be able——'

I gathered up all my courage.

'You mean they may still——"

'Well, if you must know. . . . He wants me . . . to tell you that he's saved your life, but——'

'But what?'

271

'Let his Bonds be Loosened'

'He says . . . he says that he can't save your eyes!'

My wife's outburst threw me into a state of utter confusion. At first I could make nothing of my own thoughts. They raced hither and thither, in conflict with one another. The impulse to make some passionate protest was smothered by a mocking spirit of resignation. I felt that my wife was watching me anxiously and waiting for me to say something. I made a queer little grimace.

'After all, I suppose I've seen enough in my life.' That was all I said. A painful silence followed my words. She obviously did not know what to make of it, for she had expected either some proof that it was a shock to me or a rush of impatient questions. On the face of it, it seemed natural that I should ask questions. Why had Olivecrona come to this alarming conclusion? And what exactly did it mean? Was I to *remain* in this semi-darkness or was the process to end, as the Budapest optician warned me, in the utter blackness of night? Had I been operated on too late to repair the damage to my fundus? They had said that points of atrophy were already visible. Was it *that* which it was too late to remedy? Would the atrophy continue its work of destruction to the bitter end?

I asked none of these questions. In her embarrassment, my wife got up and went over to the window. She could not explain my attitude. Ought she to look upon her husband as a hero or as an idiot?

The truth was, I was neither the one nor the other. Let me tell the truth.

'Let his Bonds be Loosened'

Every one remembers the adventure story of Michael Strogoff and his ride from Moscow to Irkutsk. In the most exciting chapter of Verne's tale the Tsar's courier is discovered and arrested, because he cannot bear to see his mother whipped in front of him. The Tartar khan orders his eyes to be put out, and, after a triumphal feast, he is bound to a tree and the torturer passes a red-hot sword before his eyes. His mother collapses, but her son manages to crawl up to her with his singed eyelids. 'You must tell no one,' he whispers. 'It shall remain our secret, for I must carry the Tsar's message to Irkutsk. But I can tell you . . . I still have my sight! The mutilation failed—perhaps because my eyes were so full of tears when I fancied I was seeing you for the last time. . . .'

I never thought of Jules Verne's story, but something similar to it must have been encouraging me. The ominous news had not really sunk below the surface of my conscious mind. A gay, almost impertinent little laugh gurgled and capered in me—a suspicion, which grew ever more sure of itself, that Olivecrona was wrong. I did not intend to say anything until I felt quite certain. On Kerstin's face I had noticed several expressions which until then had escaped me, while I had stared at Olivecrona one day in amazement before answering his question, as I had only just realized that he had blue eyes—a cold, observant yet kindly blue. And I began to notice the plate too, and the spoon, and the eiderdown. . . . This was why I made no passionate protest against the threat of going blind. I dared not contradict him until I could feel absolute confidence in my power to challenge the verdict of all-powerful science. In my heart, however, I felt an impulse to say, 'Don't you be so sure. . . !' The belief we all entertain that we are exceptions to the rule encouraged me to defy the law. According to the rules of medicine, I might be doomed to lose my eyesight, but they had forgotten that *I* was also to be taken into account. I therefore bided my time, and waited quietly for a chance to have my say.

My wife went home at five o'clock, leaving me with one of our Budapest friends, who happened to be staying in Sweden. A romantic soul who lives under the spell of art and other manifestations of beauty, Anni came to me just at an auspicious moment. I made her give me a long description of Stockholm, with its canals, its splendid gardens, its gay-coloured sailing-boats and bridges that I was soon to know. Since the days when I first wrote poems a great mass of Hungarian and German verse has been stored up in my mind, and this was an occasion for me to put my memory to the test. For hours I went on reciting poems to Anni, supporting myself in a half-sitting posture in the bed. I revelled in my success with an affectation of modesty, like an actor tricking himself out with the plumage of others. As a diversion, I treated her to a number of more or less spicy jokes, so that the humorist in me should not go without his share of praise.

That night I slept well, though I asked for only half

my usual dose of sleeping draught, as they had promised to remove my bandages the following morning.

This ceremony took place at half-past ten. Olivecrona and Söjkvist performed the solemn rite together. I closed my eyes in a delirium of enjoyment, as I listened to the tiny sounds of the scissors and gauze which told me they were cutting into and removing the gigantic helmet. The relief at being delivered, ounce by ounce, from the tremendous weight on my head was like that which I imagine a diver experiences on rising to the surface of the sea. Eventually, I was allowed to look at myself in the mirror. I had only a light cloth beret on my head, and I was delighted to see that my hair had not been cut in the front, as I imagined, and that even at the back of my head it was beginning to grow again. I had had a shave that morning, and my smooth face showed terribly thin and flabby. I found it irresistibly comic when my big mouth, spreading from ear to ear, and my broad nose tried to form an encouraging, modest little smile, like a happy bride with a garland of orange blossom. . . .

I asked the doctors for permission to sit on the edge of the bed with my feet dangling, but this was again refused. At lunch time a Hungarian journalist who was passing through Stockholm paid me a hurried visit. His cheery mood proved infectious. He had been sampling a few glasses of Swedish punch and was bubbling over with the latest news from Budapest. When Olivecrona looked in for a moment he stood up and made him

'Let his Bonds be Loosened'

a speech in German fit to make one's hair stand on end. 'Im Namen von Ungarn, etc., etc.' Olivecrona looked thoroughly embarrassed, and, making a hurried excuse, fled the field. (Afterwards, he asked me in a cautious way what it was all about. I explained that it was merely an old Hungarian custom. . . .)

At three o'clock I was left alone for a moment, and, after looking cautiously round the room, I proceeded to put myself through a test which I had decided upon in advance. On the glass slab covering my bed-table lay the book I had made ready for this purpose—Thomas Mann's story of Joseph. With this book in front of me on the eiderdown I put on the spectacles I had used for three years and began to turn the pages. My heart was beating as recklessly as a gambler's when his eyes fall on the card upon which he has ventured the highest stake of his life. I did not need to study it for long. Page 73 was still turned down, as it had been six weeks ago, when I realized that I could not go on reading even with a magnifying glass. I turned on about as far as Rózsi had read aloud to me on my sick bed, until I reached page 237. I remembered that she had left off at a passage where some wandering merchants—Ishmaelites—come upon Joseph in the well. The chief merchant sends his son Kedma to bring Joseph to the surface.

When my wife came back, I had a message for her.

'Let his Bonds be Loosened'

'Please listen to me for a moment. I want you to convey something to the Viking.'

With a certain amount of hesitation, but in an even tone, I began to read aloud.

'He was sitting bound, with his head sunk forward, and about him was an odour of the grave. . . . His wounds had almost healed. His swollen eyes were so far cured that he could open them once more. . . .

'He sat looking at his rescuers with a gentle curiosity. . . . He even smiled at their surprise. . . .

'"Let his bonds be loosened, as it is fitting that they should be, and bring him milk that he may quench his thirst. . . ."

'He drank so eagerly that a part of the milk poured from his lips before he could swallow it, as from the mouth of a suckling. . . .'

Quarter of an hour later I was in the ophthalmic section. This time I could read the word *Ögon* over the door for myself. The doctor with the reserved manner examined me for some time without speaking, but he did not inform me, as on the first occasion, that the diagnosis was no concern of mine. I heard him murmur something, as he put down the ophthalmoscope—something that was not a professional opinion, nor does it figure in any list of terms proper to science. This is what I heard him murmuring:

'*Ein Wunder*! It's a miracle!'

Later on, other doctors came to see me in my room, one of whom was not even attached to the hospital. He

'Let his Bonds be Loosened'

was a German optician on the staff of another clinic, who was abroad for purposes of study. Towards evening a photographer appeared and my head was photographed from the front and back. They informed me that the pictures were being taken on behalf of a scientific review.

On May 25th, three weeks after the operation, I was plunged in calculations of time, which now turned only upon hours, as is usually the case with prisoners. When Olivecrona called to see me I told him that I should go mad if he did not allow me to sit up on my bed. He went out again, after merely reassuring me. I had no idea what he proposed to do about it. Next day, May 26th, he came in when I was not expecting a visit from him.

'Well, what's the news?'

'I want to sit on the edge of my bed. . . .'

'You want to sit? Why sit? Get up and walk!'

I felt as if I were living through a scene from the Bible. I sat up, carefully lifted my legs one after the other out of the bed and put them on the floor. Then I stood up. It was something like the moment when a tight-rope walker, at the culminating point of his career, sets out, balancing his arms, to cross Niagara. I took a couple of steps, rested and went on again.

'You're doing all right!' I heard Olivecrona say in a casual tone, as if it were nothing to write home about. 'When d'you want to go out?'

His matter-of-fact tone sobered me down a little.

Jokingly—though the laugh was really on the wrong side of my face—I answered:

'To-morrow.'

'Just as you like. You can leave the hospital to-morrow, if you want to.'

26

Crusoe's Island

Grand Hotel, Saltjöbaden. For ten days, I had been
here convalescing in a ground-floor room opening on
to the park. Through the hall one went straight down
to the sea-shore, where, on a low pedestal, there stood a
statue of a runner. At the water's edge was a delightful
naiad. Sailing-boats and motor-launches disported
themselves in the mild spring air. In front of the hotel
there was a curve in the bay and the dome of the
Observatory stood out conspicuously on its hill. Except
for a slight feverishness I already felt quite well again,
but I had not yet succeeded in controlling my emotions.
I had become as sensitive as a baby and as sentimental
as a little kitchen-maid. A sense of pity welled up in me
for man and beast and plant. I felt sympathy with all
things living or merely bearing some semblance to
living creatures, such as even the influenza microbe.
If I happened to hear of some tiny misfortune suffered
by a stranger the tears would come to my eyes. One
evening I actually had to turn my head away because
of the forlorn expression of a little china dog in the corridor which some one must have won in a raffle.

Crusoe's Island

Before dinner I always went for coffee to a little teashop known as the *Roda Stugan*, the Red Cottage. The Fröken would place the coffee-pot, the cup and saucer before me one after the other, and each time I would repeat mechanically one of the few Swedish words I had learnt: 'Tack'—'Thank you.' Then it would be *Tack* again, and still more *Tack* and *Tack-tack*. . . . In the end, I found myself tick-tacking like an alarm clock. I felt that, as a conversation, this hadn't much to be said for it, yet I wanted to establish some sort of contact with the fair Solveig, who had perhaps recognized me already as her Peer Gynt come home at last, but lacked the means to tell me. I tried to explain myself with hands and feet, and twisted English and German words in the hope that it would make them clear to her. I pointed to the window, then to my heart, in an effort to tell her of my abounding joy in the spring, the sea, the yachts, and the green hills. Fröken looked thoughtful for a moment, then said 'So!' drawing in her breath with a surprised little sigh, as is the way in Sweden. Then she motioned me along the passage to a place where, above a little door, was written the name of the sex to which I belong. I paid my bill in disgust, and roundly told her in my own mother tongue what I thought of her intelligence—this time not in the hope that she would understand, but rather the contrary.

At eleven o'clock in the evening it was still quite light, though from eight o'clock onwards the lights of the town were already on. Never had I seen so attractive and many-coloured a town, or so fairy-like a shimmer of blues and greens and reds. I was taken to Saltjöbaden by car, and they had begun by showing me the gardens and the banks of the neighbouring canals. In the distance, I could see the golden dome of the Town Hall, at which I had gazed so often and so longingly from the hospital window. I saw palatial homes standing peacefully side by side with workmen's cottages. On one canal I was particularly taken with the blue and yellow sailing-boats. Each one had a wooden saint on the prow, carved by the peasant owners for vessels of which the cargo is also exclusively of timber. This they unload on the quayside and wait patiently for purchasers, if need be all the summer. They have their homes on board, where they live on a diet in which cheese and brandy are important items—a law-abiding and no doubt happy race of men. In fact, every one seemed happy in Sweden as they went about their business, sat on the benches, or leant, dreaming, over the blue water. At first, I told myself that this was only the same illusion I suffer from in every foreign city. It all looked so different, unreal, and fairy-like to my eyes for the simple reason that it was not my home. In toylike streets toy men and women seemed to walk about, to eat like toys and pay with toy money. After having talked to a number of Swedes I began to see the explanation for this atmosphere of calm. The Swedish nation has never been at war for a hundred and twenty years. In consequence, it has formed a habit of reckoning the value of things according to their intrinsic quality and staying power. The stone house must last for a thousand years, and the body of flesh and bone for a hundred —not merely until bombs or gunfire choose to destroy them. Happiness they look upon as man's natural state, and misfortune as something opposed to nature.

I had strolled one morning into the sunshine by the sea. Not far away, a slim, fair young girl was running up and down speaking to the passers-by, as if she were looking for some one. I saw her turn round suddenly and come running towards me like the wind. I hesitated and finally stood up.

'Uncle! Uncle!'

She fell laughing into my arms and kissed me enthusiastically. At the hall door her mother, a white-haired woman in a grey coat, was waiting for us. Gizi had not changed much in those twenty-five years, except as regards the white hair. My sister and niece had arrived from Oslo by the morning train, bringing me a friendly message from my brother-in-law, a former ship's captain, together with an injunction to take care of his family during the three days they were to spend in Stockholm.

Noemi was now twenty-one years of age.

Late that evening my new-found niece and I went for a long walk through the twilit park and along the sea-shore. Unfortunately, she did not know a word of Hungarian, as her mother never anticipated that she would have an occasion to use it. Thanks, however, to her eager curiosity, my hesitating English and German gradually became more fluent. What was I to tell my little Norwegian niece, Nini, about the country which to me meant so much and of which she had only the vague picture suggested to a girl's mind by the gipsy music of Imre Magyari! In her Norwegian home she must often have talked about the distant nations of a Europe that seemed very far away. Perhaps she had even felt curious about her writer uncle, whom she was to meet as a result of his strange adventure, and while the traces of it were still fresh on him.

Well, Nini, you ask me if I feel pleased with myself now that I am free to begin life over again in the Land of Promise where I had been laying up my treasures. Or do I still feel dazed, like a shipwrecked man to whom a wave has offered the bounty of life's remaining years? The answer is not so simple. Believe me, Nini, I should not be a really happy man, even if I were full of the most abounding confidence. Don't imagine I should be upset by the idea of having suffered a physical shipwreck. Perhaps I am a shipwrecked man in any case, but, if so, it is no consequence of what happened to me in Stockholm. It goes back much further than that, both in my life and in the lives of us all.

You look surprised, Nini, by the casual way I seem to be talking of myself as a shipwrecked man at the moment when my life has been saved. Yet it is not ingratitude which causes me to look round at this arid island and to see that, as far as I am concerned, it must remain lonely and desolate. . . . What I mean is. . . . As I see things. . . . Look here, Nini, what on earth was I starting to tell you? Just let me collect my thoughts for a moment. . . . They're still apt to go wool-gathering, you know. It's only to be expected. Those jolly old waves gave me a shake-up while they were about it! Though that wasn't the real shipwreck. . . .

The real shipwreck. . . . You must have heard, Nini, of that old Hungary before the war. You've probably pictured it to yourself as best you could. It was like one of those proud ships over there, with all her canvas swelling to the wind. . . . You have heard how the storm broke, and the ship pitched and strained. You were told how she crashed on to the rocks and lay there, breaking up, with her mast leaning over towards the horizon. That ship was ours, Nini, and she was carrying a fine cargo! I don't know on what Cape of Good Hope lay the harbour for which she was making, but I do know that we were planning to barter our rich cargo for the diamonds of some enchanted land.

Well, Nini, that's all over and done with. The beautiful cargo is no more—the coloured crystals, the flashing jewels, the perfumed attar of roses. Finished the thousand pretty trifles and the gay knick-knacks. . . . This cannot seem other than an arid island to me.

You wonder why I am in such confounded good spirits in spite of everything?

There's a reason for that, too, Nini. Let me tell you. . . . That ship you have pictured to yourself on your high Norwegian rock was only one vessel in the great fleet of civilization, and for many a long year that fleet had ceased to be the safe armada most people thought it. I was far from being the only one who felt that it no longer offered us the same security. Every moment lived in it was in some ways a disquieting experience, and this would have been the case had I enjoyed any abundance of riches. I wonder whether you will understand me when I say that, in the depths of my heart, I always felt that each one of us was alone and abandoned. What we really needed to know was not whether our ship would bring her wealth safely to harbour, but whether the storm that was to smash her to pieces would save each one of us a plank from the debris to which we might cling. For the rumblings of a submarine earthquake were already audible, though not every one in the ships heard them. Those who thought that our ambitious armada would carry on are dead now, sitting with blinded pride in their eyes on the velvet divans of the sea floor. . . .

When it came, the wreck left me alive. It flung me on to the coast with a warning that what I had to look forward to now was no longer the *maximum* but the *minimum* with which I could begin my life afresh. I was to live in the world like a shipwrecked man walking on Crusoe's island, where he had been flung when the ship on which he was travelling sank under him. I took as a welcome gift all the most trifling debris of that ship which the waves brought to me. I began to forget what life could not offer and to appreciate what it could, to accept from my debtor the thousandth part of what he owed me and to forgo the rest. I learnt to declare myself satisfied if my creditor exacted only one pound of flesh and removed only one skin in exchange for the debt I had so recklessly contracted.

On Crusoe's island, Nini, I see now that there is little point in crying out against the injustice of man or the cruelty of Fate, for, if my friend betrays and my brother in arms deceives me, a foreigner whom I never knew comes forward and saves my life. I might have been murdered, like so many others, but the only bones that were broken in me were those which allowed the forces of destruction to be taken from my head, and my skin to be made whole.

But I see something shining on the sand of Crusoe's island! The waves have flung me a present! O unutterable joy Eureka! It's a broken spoon! Let me run and fetch it quickly. . . . With this spoon I shall start digging until I come to the firm rock. Then I shall begin to build—d'you hear?—and, in a year or so, a palace will rise up on this deserted shore. . . .

D'you remember, Nini, what Caesar said on the soil of Egypt?

'He who hopes for nothing can never know despair.'

As for me, I have long had no exaggerated hopes, but I am happy to thank my Hungarian friends for allowing me to continue my life and realize such hopes as I have. I thank, too, all those who have in any way taken trouble on my behalf. I thank those strangers who gave me their prayers. I thank you, Nini, for listening so patiently to me, though I see you have already noticed that the young man I introduced to you this morning has been watching us over there for several minutes now. . . . I thank Olivecrona for the years he has given back to me. And I thank the reader for the kind and gracious attention which he has accorded to my story. . . .

At half-past six one evening we boarded the *Britannia* at Gothenburg on the first stage of our return to Hungary, via England. The horizon opened before me in all its immensity. And so, at the age of forty-seven, I set out upon my first sea voyage.